TRUST

THE RUSSELL SAGE FOUNDATION SERIES ON TRUST

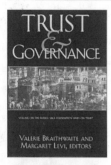

TRUST AND GOVERNANCE

VALERIE BRAITHWAITE AND MARGARET LEVI, EDITORS

"The variety of perspectives offered in this study is impressively helpful to understanding whether and how civic trust matters. The essays are best taken as a whole, since each serves a specific objective in this broadly conceived investigation." — *Choice*
Vol. I $45.00 cloth

TRUST IN SOCIETY

KAREN S. COOK, EDITOR

"An impressive collection of essays by distinguished social scientists. Arrayed across three parts—conceptions of trust; social consequences and bases of trust; and network, organization, and institutional bases of trust—the thirteen essays demonstrate that the new interest in the dynamics of trust is well placed. Each essay is a gem in its own right."
—Jonathan H. Turner, University of California, Riverside
Vol. II $45.00 cloth

EVOLUTION AND THE CAPACITY FOR COMMITMENT

RANDOLPH M. NESSE, EDITOR

"Exploring the actual emotional makeup of our species while firmly staying within an evolutionary framework, this volume spells out better than any before what is wrong with a narrow focus on human selfishness."
—Frans de Waal, Emory University
Vol. III $42.50 cloth

TRUST AND TRUSTWORTHINESS

RUSSELL HARDIN

The culmination of important new research into the roles of trust in our society, and a challenging new voice in the current discourse about the origins of cooperative behavior.
Vol. IV $32.50 cloth

 **RUSSELL SAGE FOUNDATION**

At bookstores now or call 1-800-524-6401
112 East 64th Street, New York, NY 10021
www.russellsage.org

Evolution and Human Behavior

Official Journal of The Human Behavior and Evolution Society

Volume 23, Number 3, 2002

ELSEVIER

Evolution and Human Behavior is cited in Current Contents, Excerpta Medica, Psychological Abstracts, and Sociological Abstracts.

EVOLUTION AND HUMAN BEHAVIOR is published bimonthly by Elsevier Science Inc., 655 Avenue of the Americas, New York, NY 10010. 2002 subscription rates for customers in *all countries except Europe and Japan:* Institutional rate, US$705, Personal rate, US$291. For customers in *Europe:* Institutional rate, Euro 630, Personal rate, Euro 260. For customers in *Japan:* Institutional rate, ¥83,600, Personal rate, ¥34,500. Prices include postage and are subject to change without notice. All full members of the Human Behavior and Evolution Society receive the Journal as a benefit of membership.

Orders, claims, and product enquiries: please contact the Customer Support Department at the Regional Sales Office nearest you:

New York: Elsevier Science, PO Box 945, New York, NY 10159-0945, USA; phone: (+1) (212) 633 3730 [toll free number for North American customers: 1-888-4ES-INFO (437-4636)]; fax: (+1) (212) 633 3680; e-mail: usinfo-f@elsevier.com

Amsterdam: Elsevier Science, PO Box 211, 1000 AE Amsterdam, The Netherlands; phone: (+31) 20 4853757; fax: (+31) 20 4853432; e-mail: nlinfo-f@elsevier.nl

Tokyo: Elsevier Science, 9-15 Higashi-Azabu 1-chome, Minato-ku, Tokyo 106-0044, Japan; phone: (+81) (3) 5561 5033; fax: (+81) (3) 5561 5047; e-mail: info@elsevier.co.jp

Singapore: Elsevier Science, No. 1 Temasek Avenue, #17-01 Millenia Tower, Singapore 039192; phone: (+65) 434 3727; fax: (+65) 337 2230; e-mail: asiainfo@elsevier.com.sg

Rio de Janeiro: Elsevier Science, Rua Sete de Stembro 111/16 Andar, 20050-002 Centro, Rio de Janeiro - RJ, Brazil; phone: (+55) (21) 509 5340; fax: (+55) (21) 507 1991; e-mail: elsevier@campus.com.br [Note (Latin America): for orders, claims and help desk information, please contact the Regional Sales Office in New York as listed above]

Claims for missing issues can be honored only up to three months for domestic addresses, six months for foreign addresses. Duplicate copies will not be sent to replace ones undelivered through failure to notify Elsevier of change of address.

Single copy and back volume information available upon request. Please direct orders for this journal, changes of address, and claims for missing issues to: Journals Fulfillment Department, Elsevier Science Publishing Co., Inc., 655 Avenue of the Americas, New York, NY 10010.

Advertising information. Advertising orders and enquiries can be sent to: **USA, Canada and South America:** Mr. Tino de Carlo, The Advertising Department, Elsevier Science Inc., 655 Avenue of the Americas, New York, NY 10010-5107, USA; phone: (+1) (212) 633 3815; fax: (+1) (212) 633 3820; e-mail: t.decarlo@elsevier.com. **Japan:** The Advertising Department, Elsevier Science K.K., 9-15 Higashi-Azabu 1-chome, Minato-ku, Tokyo 106-0044, Japan; phone: (+81) (3) 5561 5033; fax (+81) (3) 5561 5047. **Europe and ROW:** Rachel Gresle-Farthing, The Advertising Department, Elsevier Science Ltd., The Boulevard, Langford Lane, Kidlington, Oxford OX5 IGB, UK; phone: (+44) (1865) 843565; fax: (+44) (1865) 843976; e-mail: r.gresle-farthing@elsevier.co.uk

ELSEVIER

Evolution and Human Behavior 23 (2002) 159–166

Evolution
and Human
Behavior

Reactions to children's faces
Resemblance affects males more than females

Steven M. Platek, Rebecca L. Burch, Ivan S. Panyavin,
Brett H. Wasserman, Gordon G. Gallup, Jr.*

Department of Psychology, State University of New York at Albany, Albany, NY 12222, USA

Received 31 July 2001; received in revised form 22 August 2001; accepted 27 September 2001

Abstract

Since cuckoldry risk is asymmetrical, we hypothesized that parental investment would be more affected by paternal than maternal resemblance. To test this hypothesis, we asked subjects hypothetical questions about investing in children under conditions in which their faces or those of other people had been morphed with photographs of children. Males were more likely to choose a face they had been morphed with as the most attractive, the child they were most likely to adopt, the child they would like to spend the most time with, the child they would spend US$50 on, and the child they would least resent having to pay child support for. Reactions to children's faces by females were much less affected by resemblance. © 2002 Elsevier Science Inc. All rights reserved.

Keywords: Paternal resemblance; Cuckoldry; Paternal uncertainty

1. Introduction

Males invest less in children that they are not biologically related to and in many cases are more likely to abuse step or otherwise unrelated children (Anderson, Kaplan, Lam, & Lancaster, 1999; Daly & Wilson, 1988, 1996; Marlowe, 1999). According to Daly and Wilson (1998) there are two ways in which a male can increase the probability that the children he is caring for are carrying his genetic material: he can monitor and/or

---

* Corresponding author. Tel.: +1-518-442-4852; fax: +1-518-442-4867.
E-mail address: gallup@csc.albany.edu (G.G. Gallup, Jr.).

sequester the female partner during the period that she is fertile to reduce the risk of being cuckolded, or he can attempt to assess paternity based on the degree to which the children resemble him.

There are two forms that a paternal resemblance mechanism might take: (1) the degree to which a male is told a child resembles him (i.e., a "social mirror") and (2) the degree to which the child actually resembles him. Daly and Wilson (1982) recorded spontaneous remarks in maternity wards regarding the appearance of newborn children. Mothers and their friends and relatives were more likely to comment on how children resembled their fathers than they were to say the child resembled the mother or any other family member. When fathers displayed any doubt, the mothers were quick to reassure them of the child's resemblance. Regalski and Gaulin (1993) have replicated these findings using Mexican families.

In a population of males convicted of domestic violence, Burch and Gallup (2000) found the more males felt that their children looked like them, the better the children were treated. The childhood of the abusive males themselves were also associated with how much they thought they resembled their fathers. Perceptions of paternal resemblance were correlated with the incidence of physical and sexual abuse they experienced as children, as well as feelings of closeness to their fathers.

Christenfeld and Hill (1995) found that objective raters did no better than chance at matching pictures of 1-year-old infants to their mothers, but could more accurately match the pictures of infants to their fathers. Other studies have failed to replicate these findings (Brédart & French, 1999; McLain, Setters, Moulton, & Pratt, 2000; Nesse, Silverman, & Bortz, 1990), but in these studies, actual paternity was never determined (e.g., by DNA testing). Since the incidence of cuckoldry may be appreciable (see Baker & Bellis, 1995, for a review), it is easy to see how instances of failed paternity could statistically mask/obscure paternal resemblance.

A more compelling test of the paternal resemblance hypothesis would be to experimentally manipulate resemblance to determine the effect it has on treatment and attitudes toward children. In this study, facial resemblance was manipulated using computerized facial morphing based on combinations of subjects and children and reactions to these images were measured with hypothetical investment scenarios.

2. Methods

2.1. Subjects

Forty (20 males, 20 females) undergraduates were recruited from the State University of New York at Albany as subjects and received course credit for their participation. Subjects were informed ahead of time that they would be participating in a study that required having their picture taken and that they were going to be asked questions about childcare. The study was approved by the local institutional review board and all subjects gave written informed consent.

2.2. Pictures

Pictures of subjects were taken using a Hewlett Packard Model 315 digital camera. Subjects were asked not to smile or frown for the picture and to try to maintain a neutral unexpressive face. The images were processed using a 233-mHz PC and Paint Shop Pro (version 3.11) software. All images were converted to 256 shades of gray, cropped just under the chin, from ear to ear, and just below the hairline, and images were centered. All images were made the same size (200×150 pixels) and brightness using the color editor and histogram rectification properties in Paint Shop Pro. The images were mounted on a white background.

While they waited, each subject's picture was morphed (Ulead Morph Editor, version 1.0) with the image of either a female or male 2-year-old child so that the stimulus picture represented a combination of the subject and the child in a 50:50 ratio. Twenty subjects (10 males, 10 females) were morphed with the image of the female child and 20 subjects (10 males, 10 females) were morphed with the image of the male child. The morphing program allowed us to set reference points to combine two images (a start and an end image) into one. For example, on the starting image (e.g., the subject's face), one can place a reference point over the pupil and the computer automatically places a corresponding reference point over the end image (e.g., the child's face). However, the point on the child's face may not be aligned with the pupil (it may fall on the cheek or the forehead). Using the computer mouse, the reference point in the end image can be moved, without affecting the reference point in the start image, to align it with the pupil so that in the morph image these two points are merged together into one. In the morphing/merging process, we used approximately 40 reference points for each image. Presets were used to control the number of pixels from a starting and an ending image that was entered into the morphed image and these values could be changed actively. As shown in Fig. 1, the program then rectifies the image on a two-dimensional plane so that it appears as a real and undistorted combination of the two faces.

2.3. Design

The entire experiment was computerized using SuperLab (Cedrus, version 2.01). As shown in Fig. 2, each trial consisted of the subject being shown five faces on the computer screen arranged in a semicircular array with a question embedded in the middle (e.g., "Which of these children would you spend the most time with?"). Each face was also labeled with a letter and subjects made their choices by pressing the corresponding letter on a computer keyboard (see Fig. 2).

There were two types of arrays. Both involved five faces. The first contained one image of the subject's face morphed with the image of a toddler and four other people's faces morphed with that same toddler's face. The second array contained five other people's faces morphed with the toddler's face. Each face array was presented 10 times; once with each of 10 questions (see Table 1). All face position coordinates within an array were randomized between questions so that no face appeared in the same position

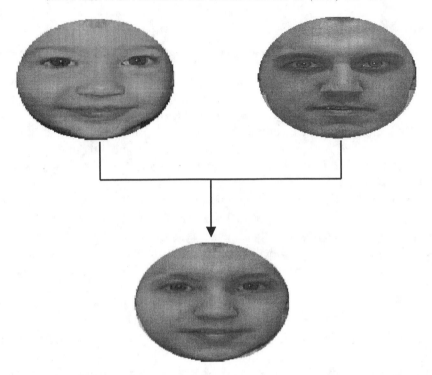

Fig. 1. A representative 50% self–child morph constructed from the image of (on the right) a subject and a male child (on the left).

on every trial. The two face arrays were sampled randomly until each question had been presented within each array.

Latency to respond was recorded for all questions by SuperLab as the elapsed time (ms) between presentation of an array and a subject's response. At the end of the experiment, subjects were asked how they made their choices and whether they used any particular strategy when selecting a face out of the array. They were also asked whether it was difficult to choose faces out of the arrays.

3. Results

There was no effect of the sex of the toddler's face. A binomial test revealed that males chose the face that they had been morphed with more often than chance in response to the questions: "Which one of these children would you be most likely to adopt?", $P < .001$; "Which one of these children do you find to be the most attractive?", $P < .001$; "Which one of these children would you be MOST comfortable spending time with?", $P < .001$; "Which one of these children would you spend US$50 on if you could only spend it on one child?", $P < .001$; and "If you were forced to pay child support to these children, which one would you LEAST resent having to pay child support for?", $P < .05$. The binomial test also showed that

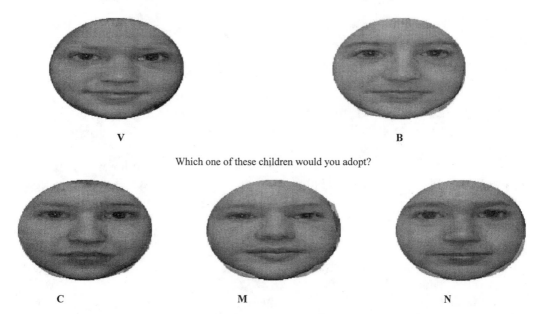

Fig. 2. A typical stimulus face array and question as it appeared on the computer screen.

males were less likely to select a face they had been morphed with in response to the question: "If one of these children damaged something valuable of yours, which one would you punish the MOST?", $P < .05$. In contrast, females only selected a face that they had been morphed with more often than chance in response to one question: "Which one of these children would you spend US$50 on if you could only spend it on one child?", $P < .05$ (see Table 1).

Table 1
Percentage of males and females who picked their self-morph in response to the different questions

	Males (%)	Female (%)
Which one of these children would you be most likely to adopt?	90**	35
Which one of these children do you find to be the most attractive?	85**	35
Which one of these children would you be comfortable spending the MOST time with?	70**	35
Which one of these children would you spend the LEAST time with?	10	10
Which one of these children would you spend US$50 on if you could only spend it on one child?	80**	40*
Which one would you spend US$50 on last?	15	30
If one of these children damaged something valuable of yours, which one would you punish MOST?	0*	15
Which one would you punish LEAST?	20	15
If you were forced to pay child support to these children, which one would you MOST resent having to pay child support for?	10	5
Which one would you LEAST resent having to pay child support for?	40*	25

   * $P < .05$.
   ** $P < .001$.

Males were also more prone than females to choose their own face–toddler morphs. Fisher's exact probability tests showed that males were more likely than females to choose their self-morph in response to the questions: "Which one of these children would you be most likely to adopt?", $P<.001$; "Which one of these children do you find to be the most attractive?", $P<.001$; "Which one of these children do you think that you would spend the most time with?", $P<.01$; and "Which one of these children would you spend US\$50 on if you could only spend it on one child?", $P<.01$. There were no questions where females were more likely than males to choose their own face–toddler morph.

Composite scores reflecting favorable responses toward morphs were created by subtracting the number of times a subject selected a self-morph in response to negative items (e.g., "If one of these children damaged something valuable of yours, which one would you punish MOST?") from the number of times a subject selected a self-morph in response to positive items (e.g., "Which one of the children would you be most likely to adopt?"). A Mann–Whitney U test applied to these scores showed that men (mean rank = 26.25) exhibited significantly more favorable reactions toward self-morphs than females (mean rank = 14.75), $P<.01$.

In the second array of faces, where the subject's face was not morphed with the child's, there were no sex differences in the likelihood of selecting any particular face and a binomial test showed that neither males nor females chose any face more often than chance.

More women (80.0%) indicated that it was difficult to choose faces from the arrays than men (45.0%), $\chi^2 = 7.20$, $P<.01$. Females also took longer to respond to all questions. When analyses were performed on individual questions, females took longer to respond ($M=21.15$ s) to "Which one of these children would you resent most if you were forced to pay child support?" than males ($M=12.43$ s), $F(1,36)=4.579$, $P<.01$. By calculating the mean reaction time for each question and then counting across all questions to determine if a subject was slower or faster than average, a Fisher's exact probability test showed that females took significantly longer to respond across all questions than males, $P<.001$.

At the end of the experiment when subjects were asked how they chose faces out of the arrays, there was little consensus. Some reported using the eyes, while others reported using the mouth or nose. Some reported making attributions about the faces, such as "I selected the face that I thought needed my help most, or looked most/least depressed."

4. Discussion

When subjects were shown their own faces morphed with a child's in an array of four other people's faces morphed with that child, males were more likely to choose the face that resembled their own as the one they would be most likely to adopt, the most attractive, the child they would spend the most time with, the child they would spend money on, and the child they would least resent having to pay child support for.

Unlike males, females were relatively indifferent to whether the children's faces resembled their own. There were no questions where females were more likely than males to choose a face that they had been morphed with. In fact, females took longer to respond to all questions, and more women than men expressed difficulty in choosing faces. Whereas in self-morph arrays males chose which child to support or punish quickly and easily, females took longer to deliberate and attempted to distribute their choices across faces.

It is interesting to note that the subjects were unaware of the effect resemblance had on their choices. When queried about their choices at the conclusion of the experiment, none identified resemblance as a factor in how they chose which child to support or punish, nor did they even realize that their faces had been morphed with the child. During debriefing, subjects were told that their face had been morphed with some of the faces, and they were given the opportunity to view the faces again. But none could pick their self-morph out of the array. It was not until the real, unmorphed picture of the subject and the self-morph were aligned next to each other on the computer screen that they could identify their morph, and subjects expressed surprise that they had been unable to see their own features embedded in the face of the child.

During human evolutionary history, it would have behooved females to ascribe paternal resemblance for purposes of securing paternal investment. However, it is possible that the degree to which a female ascribes resemblance to the ostensible father may correlate with her sexual infidelity. In other words, increasing the chances of successfully cuckolding her mate may have rested on the female's ability to deceive the male into believing that he was the child's father. As a result, one might expect males to have evolved a counter strategy, i.e., assessing the actual degree to which a child resembles him in order to make a more accurate determination about paternity. Our data suggest that males do use resemblance as a factor in their reactions towards children and it appears that this may be operating at a relatively unconscious level.

The fact that resemblance plays a greater role on how males react toward children is consistent with the literature regarding treatment of unrelated children and how paternal resemblance impacts child abuse and investment (Anderson et al., 1999; Burch & Gallup, 2000; Daly & Wilson, 1996; Marlowe, 1999; but see Case, Lin, & McLanahan, 2001). It is interesting to note that the largest difference between males and females in our study was in response to the question "Which one of these children would you be most likely to adopt?" As shown in Table 1, 18 out of 20 males, or almost three times as many men as women picked the self-morph picture of the child as the one they would most likely adopt. Not only are these results consistent with expectations based on paternal resemblance theory, but they may have important implications for adoption policy. Our data suggest that by matching characteristics of an adopted child to those of an adoptive father, the likelihood of achieving a long-term positive outcome might be enhanced. In the context of the prominent role that males play in instances of child abuse and family violence, it is also interesting to note that none of the males picked children's faces that resembled their own as the child they would the most likely to punish.

Acknowledgments

The authors thank Julian Paul Keenan, Sid O'Bryant, Carlos Finlay, and Anthony, Michelle, and Joseph Rubino for their assistance with computer software and design materials.

References

Anderson, K., Kaplan, H., Lam, D., & Lancaster, J. (1999). Paternal care of genetic fathers and stepfathers: II. Reports by Xhosa high school students. *Evolution and Human Behavior, 20*, 433–451.

Baker, R. R., & Bellis, M. A. (1995). *Human sperm competition: copulation, masturbation, and infidelity.* London: Chapman & Hall.

Brédart, S., & French, R. (1999). Do babies resemble their fathers more than their mothers? A failure to replicate Christenfeld and Hill. *Evolution and Human Behavior, 20*, 129–135.

Burch, R. L., & Gallup Jr., G. G. (2000). Perceptions of paternal resemblance predict family violence. *Evolution and Human Behavior, 21*, 429–435.

Case, A., Lin, I.-F., & McLanahan, S. (2001). Educational attainment of siblings in stepfamilies. *Evolution and Human Behavior, 22*, 269–289.

Christenfeld, N., & Hill, E. (1995). Whose baby are you? *Nature, 378*, 669.

Daly, M., & Wilson, M. (1982). Whom are newborn babies said to resemble? *Ethology and Sociobiology, 3*, 69–78.

Daly, M., & Wilson, M. (1988). Evolutionary social psychology and family homicide. *Science, 242*, 519–524.

Daly, M., & Wilson, M. (1996). Violence against stepchildren. *Current Directions in Psychological Science, 5*, 77–81.

Daly, M., & Wilson, M. (1998). *The truth about Cinderella: a Darwinian view of parental love.* New Haven, CT, USA: Yale University Press.

Marlowe, F. (1999). Showoffs or providers? The parenting effort of Hadza men. *Evolution and Human Behavior, 20*, 391–404.

McLain, D. K., Setters, D., Moulton, M. P., & Pratt, A. E. (2000). Ascription of resemblance of newborns by parents and nonrelatives. *Evolution and Human Behavior, 21*, 11–23.

Nesse, R., Silverman, A., & Bortz, A. (1990). Sex differences in ability to recognize family resemblance. *Ethology and Sociobiology, 11*, 11–21.

Regalski, J., & Gaulin, S. (1993). Whom are Mexican infants said to resemble? Monitoring and fostering paternal confidence in the Yucatan. *Ethology and Sociobiology, 14*, 97–113.

ELSEVIER

Evolution and Human Behavior 23 (2002) 167–171

Evolution
and Human
Behavior

Bowling with our imaginary friends

Satoshi Kanazawa

Department of Sociology, Indiana University of Pennsylvania, Indiana, PA 15705-1087, USA

Received 14 August 2001; received in revised form 30 October 2001; accepted 31 October 2001

Abstract

Putnam [J. Democracy 6 (1995). *Bowling Alone: The Collapse and Revival of American Community* (2000). New York: Simon & Schuster.] claims that Americans are socially and civically disengaged because they watch too much TV. I contend that, because evolved psychological mechanisms have difficulty comprehending entities that did not exist in the environment of evolutionary adaptedness (EEA), humans should fail to distinguish between real friends and the imaginary ones they see on TV. Consistent with my contention, the analysis of the US General Social Survey (GSS) data indicates that people who watch certain types of TV are more satisfied with their friendships as if they had more friends and socialized with them more often. © 2002 Elsevier Science Inc. All rights reserved.

Keywords: Robert D. Putnam; *Bowling Alone*; Social capital; Television

In his highly influential work, *Bowling Alone*, Putnam (1995, 2000) argues that social capital and community in the United States have declined in the past half century. Americans no longer participate in voluntary associations (such as churches, labor unions, and neighborhood bowling leagues) as much as they used to. Putnam (1995, p. 75) attributes at least part of this decline in social capital to TV viewing. "Television has made our communities (or, rather, what we experience as our communities) wider and shallower." Americans now are socially and civically disengaged because they spend too much time watching TV.

Evolutionary psychology, however, provides an alternative perspective on the simultaneous decline in civic engagement and rise in TV viewing in the United States. A

E-mail address: kanazawa@grove.iup.edu (S. Kanazawa).

fundamental premise of evolutionary psychology is that the human brain and its psycho-logical mechanisms are adapted to the environment of evolutionary adaptedness (EEA), in which they evolved and for which they were designed, and they are not necessarily adaptive in the current environment (Tooby & Cosmides, 1990). The human brain and its psycho-logical mechanisms should therefore be strongly biased to view and respond to the environment as if it were still the EEA, and they should have difficulty comprehending and dealing with entities and situations that did not exist in the EEA.

Perhaps the best example of the unconscious difficulty the human brain has in dealing with entities and situations that did not exist in the EEA is the effect of pornography on men and women. The only biological function of an erection is to allow men to have intercourse with women. Yet today men have erections when they look at naked women in photographs and videos, even though it is absolutely impossible for the men to copulate with these women. This is probably because there were no photographs and videos in the EEA, where every image of a sexually responsive woman was a live woman, with whom there was some possibility of copulation. It therefore paid in reproductive terms for the ancestral men to have erections to be ready for copulation every time they saw images of sexually responsive naked women. Men unconsciously act as if they could copulate with the women they see in pornographic photographs and videos because these entities did not exist in the EEA.

An overwhelming majority of consumers of pornography throughout the world are men. Because promiscuous and casual sex carries far greater biological and reproductive costs for women than it does for men, it makes perfect sense for women to avoid promiscuous sex with a large number of partners in real life. However, it is absolutely impossible for women to conceive by watching naked men in sexual situations in photographs and videos. There is thus no reason for women to avoid exposure to pornography; the consumption of por-nography carries no potential reproductive costs to women. Women nonetheless do not consume pornography nearly as much as men do because their brain and its psychological mechanisms also have difficulty comprehending the images of naked men in photographs and videos for what they are and act as if exposure to such men might carry some reproductive costs, as it would have in the EEA.

The sexually dimorphic response to pornography suggests that the human brain and its psychological mechanisms have unconscious difficulty comprehending entities and situations that did not exist in the EEA. If this observation is true, then it may generalize to other artificial images of humans. Neither television nor movies existed in the EEA, where all realistic images of people with whom you encountered repeatedly were your friends and family. If you knew someone in the EEA, they also knew you; there was no "one-way" acquaintance, as there is today with celebrities, where we know them but they do not know us. If men and women unconsciously respond as if naked people in pornographic photo-graphs and videos were their potential sexual partners, then they may respond as if the people they see on television were their friends.

I would therefore predict that people who watch more TV should feel like they have more friends. Furthermore, there should be some sex differences in this pattern. Past research on personal networks in the United States demonstrates that women are more likely to have their kin among their close friends, whereas men are more likely to have coworkers among theirs (Campbell, 1988; Fischer & Oliker, 1983; Marsden, 1987), and Kanazawa (2001) explains these sex differences in terms of evolved psychological mechanisms of men and women. Then, women who watch TV shows about people in families should feel like they have more friends, while men who watch TV shows about people at work should feel like they have more friends. In contrast, Putnam's analysis would appear to predict that men and women who watch more TV of any type are less satisfied with their friends because they are socially disengaged.

The US General Social Survey (GSS) allows an empirical test of these predictions. The National Opinion Research Center at the University of Chicago has administered the GSS either annually or biennially since 1972. Personal interviews are conducted with a nationally representative sample of noninstitutionalized adults in the US. The sample size is about 1500 for each annual survey, and about 3000 for each biennial one. The exact questions asked in the survey vary by the year.

The GSS routinely asks its respondents how satisfied they are in different areas of their lives (1 = none, 2 = a little, 3 = some, 4 = a fair amount, 5 = quite a bit, 6 = a great deal, 7 = a very great deal), and one of these areas is their friendships. Note that this question measures the respondents' *subjective* assessment of their satisfaction with friendships. Table 1 shows that, controlling for age, race, education, and marital status in multiple regression equations, women and men who have more friends and who socialize more with them (measured on a 7-point scale from 1 = never to 7 = almost every day) are subjectively more satisfied with their friendships.

Table 1
The effects of real friends on satisfaction with friendships, GSS, 1986

	Women	Men
Real friends		
Number of friends	0.0192 (0.0044)****	0.0179 (0.0040)****
Socializing with friends	0.1421 (0.0268)****	0.1400 (0.0343)***
Control variables		
Age	0.0105 (0.0026)***	8.8501^{-4} (0.0032)
Race (Black = 1)	− 0.6463 (0.1201)****	− 0.4030 (0.1624)*
Education	0.0531 (0.0161)**	0.0163 (0.0148)
Marital status (married = 1)	0.2872 (0.0842)***	0.1220 (0.1034)
R^2	.1360	.0875
Number of cases	832	606

Main entries are unstandardized regression coefficients.
Numbers in parentheses are standard errors.
  * $P < .05$.
 ** $P < .01$.
*** $P < .001$.
**** $P < .0001$.
 [†] $P < .10$.

Table 2
The effects of TV friends on satisfaction with friendships, GSS, 1993

	Women			Men		
TV friends						
Dramas and sitcoms	0.0843 (0.0428)*			−0.0306 (0.0554)		
TV news		0.0500 (0.0486)			0.1423 (0.0749)†	
PBS shows			−0.0372 (0.0407)			0.1631 (0.0525)**
Control variables						
Age	0.0040 (0.0030)	0.0022 (0.0031)	0.0034 (0.0030)	−0.0058 (0.0039)	−0.0066 (0.0039)†	−0.0060 (0.0038)
Race (Black = 1)	−0.5789 (0.1595)***	−0.6007 (0.1596)***	−0.5967 (0.1598)***	−0.1925 (0.2124)	−0.2272 (0.2113)	−0.2583 (0.2099)
Education	0.0509 (0.0192)**	0.0482 (0.0194)*	0.0548 (0.0197)**	−0.0343 (0.0202)†	−0.0370 (0.0200)†	−0.0499 (0.0203)*
Marital status (married = 1)	0.1535 (0.0998)	0.1424 (0.1005)	0.1676 (0.1007)†	0.2872 (0.1323)*	0.2754 (0.1313)*	0.3021 (0.1303)*
TV hours per day	−0.0188 (0.0255)	−0.0082 (0.0248)	0.0027 (0.0250)	−0.1081 (0.0335)**	−0.1231 (0.0324)***	−0.1322 (0.0323)***
R^2	.0550	.0506	.0503	.0487	.0570	.0711
Number of cases	613	613	611	426	427	426

Main entries are unstandardized regression coefficients.
Numbers in parentheses are standard errors.

  * $P < .05$.
  ** $P < .01$.
  *** $P < .001$.
  ****$P < .0001$.
  † $P < .10$.

  Table 2 demonstrates that watching certain types of TV shows increases the respondents' satisfaction with friendships in exactly the same way. (Remember that the dependent variable does not measure a general level of happiness or satisfaction with life in general, but their satisfaction *specifically with their friendships*.) The GSS in 1993 asked its respondents how often they watched different kinds of television shows (1 = never, 2 = rarely, 3 = several times a month, 4 = several times a week, 5 = every day). Controlling for the same demographic variables and the total number of hours they spend watching TV, women who watched relatively more prime time dramas and situation comedies ("sitcoms") (a large proportion of which depict people in families and other primary groups) were significantly ($P < .05$) more satisfied with their friendships. At the same time, watching TV news or Public Broadcasting Service (PBS) programs (which, relative to prime time dramas and sitcoms, depict fewer families and more people at work) does not increase women's subjective satisfaction with friendships. The pattern is opposite for men. While watching prime time dramas and sitcoms does not increase their subjective satisfaction with friendships, watching TV news ($P < .06$) and PBS shows ($P < .01$) does.

The analysis of the GSS data therefore demonstrates that watching certain types of TV shows has the same effect on subjective satisfaction with friendships as having more friends and socializing with them more often. This is consistent with my contention that the human brain has difficulty distinguishing real friends and people they see on TV, because TV did not exist in the EEA, where every realistic image of someone you repeatedly and routinely saw was your real friend. The data are contrary to Putnam's contention that TV viewing is indicative of social disengagement. While the evidence presented here is merely suggestive and far from conclusive, I cannot think of any other reason why women should feel as if they have more friends and socialize with them more if they watch more prime time dramas and sitcoms, and men should respond similarly if they watch more TV news and PBS shows. My contention and the supportive evidence presented here suggest that, contrary to Putnam, there is nothing shallow about the community we experience by watching TV, or so our brain thinks. Watching TV *is* our form of participating in civic groups because we do not really know that we are not participating in them.

Acknowledgments

I thank Joanne Savage for disagreeing with me, thereby motivating me to write this paper; Editors for extremely helpful suggestions and for the article's title; and my colleagues at CSC (Dana Whitaker, Natalie Hurley, Dan Rydell, Jeremy Goodwin, and Casey McCall) for their love and support.

References

Campbell, K. E. (1988). Gender differences in job-related networks. *Work and Occupations, 15*, 179–200.

Fischer, C. S., & Oliker, S. J. (1983). A research note on friendship, gender, and the life cycle. *Social Forces, 62*, 124–133.

Kanazawa, S. (2001). Where do social structures come from? *Advances in Group Processes, 18*, 161–183.

Marsden, P. V. (1987). Core discussion networks of Americans. *American Sociological Review, 52*, 122–131.

Putnam, R. D. (1995). Bowling alone: America's declining social capital. *Journal of Democracy, 6*, 65–78.

Putnam, R. D. (2000). *Bowling alone: the collapse and revival of American community*. New York: Simon & Schuster.

Tooby, J., & Cosmides, L. (1990). The past explains the present: emotional adaptations and the structure of ancestral environments. *Ethology and Sociobiology, 11*, 375–424.

Evolution
and Human
Behavior

ELSEVIER   Evolution and Human Behavior 23 (2002) 173–180

The sound of symmetry
Voice as a marker of developmental instability

Susan M. Hughes, Marissa A. Harrison, Gordon G. Gallup, Jr.*

Department of Psychology, State University of New York at Albany, Albany, NY 12222, USA

Received 31 August 2001; received in revised form 16 November 2001; accepted 20 November 2001

Abstract

Low fluctuating asymmetry (FA, a measure of deviation from bilateral symmetry) appears to be a phenotypic marker of reproductive viability and health. In the present study, we investigated whether ratings of voice attractiveness were correlated with variations in FA. Several bilateral traits were measured to calculate a FA index and independent raters who did not know and never saw the subjects assessed the attractiveness of recordings of each subject's voice. Voices of subjects with greater bilateral symmetry were rated as more attractive by members of both sexes than those with asymmetrical traits. © 2002 Elsevier Science Inc. All rights reserved.

Keywords: Bilateral symmetry; Fluctuating asymmetry; Voice attractiveness; Mate choice

1. Introduction

Fluctuating asymmetry (FA) represents deviations from bilateral symmetry for different morphological traits. FA reflects an individual's ability to deal with both genetic and environmental stresses during ontogeny and has been shown to be a good index of genetic and phenotypic fitness (Thornhill & Gangestad, 1999). For instance, low FA in both sexes is associated with increased genetic, physical, and mental health (see Thornhill & Møller, 1997). In men, low FA has been shown to predict greater facial attractiveness (Gangestad, Thornhill, & Yeo, 1994; Perrett et al., 1999), lower metabolic rate (Manning, Koukourakis, & Brodie, 1997;

---

* Corresponding author. Tel.: +1-518-442-4852; fax: +1-518-442-4687.
E-mail address: gallup@csc.albany.edu (G.G. Gallup, Jr.).

Manning, Scutt, Whitehouse, & Leinster, 1997), and more muscularity and vigor (see Thornhill & Gangestad, 1999). Symmetrical males have been reported to attract a greater number of sexual partners, have sex at an earlier age (Thornhill & Gangestad, 1994), and have more extra pair copulations (Gangestad & Thornhill, 1997). Women report experiencing orgasm at higher rates with symmetric men (Thornhill, Gangestad, & Comer, 1995). In women, increased FA is correlated with increased health risks (Scutt, Manning, Whitehouse, Leinster, & Massey, 1997) and lower FA is associated with higher fertility (Manning, Koukourakis et al., 1997; Manning, Scutt et al., 1997; Møller, Soler, & Thornhill, 1995) and facial attractiveness (Perrett et al., 1999). Thus, symmetry seems to be an important indicator of genetic quality of potential mates for both sexes.

Measures of FA for some morphological traits are heritable (Livshits & Kobyliansky, 1991). Since FA variation reflects heritable fitness and is an indicator of genetic quality, one might expect to find selection for mate preferences based on FA or on traits that may covary with FA (Thornhill & Gangestad, 1999). One trait that covaries with FA is an individual's body scent. During the ovulatory phase of the menstrual cycle, females rate the body odor of men who have greater bilateral symmetry as more attractive (Gangestad & Thornhill, 1998; Thornhill & Gangestad, 1999). Just as scent may be involved in mate choice (Thornhill & Gangestad, 1999; Wedekind & Furi, 1997), vocal cues may also be important especially since they can provide information about potential mates when visual cues are ambiguous or not available. Vocal communication frees up the hands for doing other things, does not require visual contact, and allows for communication while focusing on other activities. By adjusting one's orientation and the intensity of sound production, information can be directed toward particular targets, transmitted over appreciable distances, inflections can be used for emphasis, and information can be kept relatively private by whispering (Gallup & Cameron, 1992). Possibly, the greatest advantage to vocal communication, however, is that neither the production nor the reception of sound is dependent upon light. Prior to the use of fire or other artificial lighting, gestural communication would have been limited to approximately 12 hours of daylight per day. Consequently, voice could have been an important medium for communication at night and a means of making mate assessments.

In the present study, we examined the relationship between independent ratings of voice attractiveness and bilateral symmetry in humans. Previous studies have shown that voice can be subjectively evaluated and observers show high rates of agreement (interrater reliability = .85) on judgements of voice attractiveness (Zuckerman & Driver, 1989; Zuckerman, Hodgins, & Miyake, 1990). There have been attempts to identify the physical characteristics of attractive voices using sound spectrographs, but spectrogram data leave much of the variance in voice ratings unaccounted for and subjective ratings predict voice attractiveness better than spectrographic analyses (see Miyake & Zuckerman, 1993).

Because of the recent interest in digit morphology as a correlate of different psychological features, we also examined digit length ratios. Research has shown that second digit/fourth digit ratios are influenced by prenatal exposure to sex steroids (e.g., Manning et al., 2000). Since FA is also thought to be a reflection of factors operating prenatally, we also investigated the relationship between second digit/fourth digit ratios and ratings of voice attractiveness.

2. Methods

One hundred and six undergraduate students (48 females and 58 males) from the State University of New York at Albany participated in this study. The methods and procedures we used were approved by the University Institutional Review Board. The mean age of the participants was 20.6 years (S.D. = 3.8), with ages ranging from 18 to 34. Subjects received course credit for their participation.

The study consisted of four phases. Subjects were initially asked to complete a brief demographic questionnaire, and rate approximately 15 prerecorded voices. Several bilateral morphological traits were measured for each subject and they were asked to speak into a microphone to have their own voices recorded.

Because of the possibility that the content of what subjects said could influence the perception of their voices, subjects' voices were recorded onto computer software while being asked to count from 1 to 10. This procedure was utilized in an attempt to obtain vocal samples that were both neutral and of comparable content. A microphone (Andrea NC-8) positioned approximately 2.5 cm from the subject's mouth was used to record voices. Subjects were not included if they were chronic smokers (smoked more than a pack of cigarettes a week), had a cold or illness that may have affected the way they normally spoke (i.e., severe congestion), had ever broken their nose, had surgery on their throat or larynx that affected their speech, had a hearing impairment, had auditory surgery, or had obvious accents in which English was not their first language. Six subjects were excluded for these reasons.

A total of seven anatomical traits were measured for each subject: the ventral surface of the second through the fifth digits from the basal crease to the tip of the finger, elbow width, the maximum width of the hand, and the maximum diameter of the wrist. These traits were chosen because they exhibit FA that can be measured reliably and accurately (Livshits & Kobyliansky, 1991; Martin, Manning, & Dowrick, 1999). Following the procedures used by Gangestad et al. (1994), the left and right sides of each trait were measured independently to the nearest 0.01 mm using a 15-cm electronic digital caliper (Edmt DC6). All traits were measured twice by the same experimenter and the average for each trait was computed. Subjects who had ever broken any of the bones underlying these traits or had sustained a sprain within the last 6 months were not included. Four subjects were excluded on these grounds. Our final sample consisted of 96 subjects (46 females and 50 males).

The FA's for individual traits were calculated by using the absolute difference between the left and right sides of each trait divided by the mean size of the left and right sides for that trait. Individual trait asymmetries were then summed to yield a composite FA index for each subject, termed the overall FA index (Livshits & Kobyliansky, 1991). The higher the FA score, the more asymmetrical an individual is for the trait in question. FA index scores that are averaged across several bilateral traits are thought by some people to provide a better estimate of an organism's developmental stability than any single trait (Livshits & Kobyliansky, 1991). However, analyses based on individual traits were conducted as well (see Table 1).

Ratings of anonymous voice recordings were based on a five-point scale (1 = very unattractive, 2 = somewhat unattractive, 3 = average, 4 = somewhat attractive, 5 = very

Table 1
Correlations among subjects' overall and trait-specific FA measures and judges' ratings of the attractiveness of their voices

	Voice attract	Overall FA	FA elbow	FA wrist	FA hand	FA second digit	FA third digit	FA fourth digit	FA fifth digit
Overall FA									
Pearson correlation	− .460**								
P	.000								
FA elbow									
Pearson correlation	− .053	.424**							
P	.609	.000							
FA wrist									
Pearson correlation	− .091	.402**	.158						
P	.375	.000	.125						
FA hand									
Pearson correlation	− .162	.317**	− .090	.021					
P	.115	.002	.383	.839					
FA second digit									
Pearson correlation	− .310**	.340**	− .025	− .012	− .026				
P	.002	.001	.805	.909	.799				
FA third digit									
Pearson correlation	− .045	.310**	.061	.030	.013	.080			
P	.664	.002	.555	.769	.900	.440			
FA fourth digit									
Pearson correlation	− .309**	.477**	− .030	.106	.118	.007	.107		
P	.002	.000	.773	.305	.252	.949	.301		
FA fifth digit									
Pearson correlation	− .277**	.436**	− .172	− .066	.081	− .034	− .130	.171	
P	.006	.000	.094	.522	.435	.744	.206	.096	

All correlations are based on data for 96 subjects (46 women, 50 men). See text for results of analyses with the sexes considered separately.
  ** Significant at the .01 level (two-tailed).

attractive). Each voice was rated by 15 (±2) raters who consisted of approximately equal numbers of males and females. None of the raters were given any information about the subjects whose voices had been recorded, nor were they allowed to see or in any other way identify the individuals whose voices they were rating. Subjects were asked if they recognized any of the voices, and told not to rate those they thought they knew. None of the subjects indicated recognizing any of the voice recordings. The interrater reliability for voice attractiveness ratings was reasonably high (Cronbach's alpha, $r = .881$, $P < .01$; Kendall coefficient of concordance, $W = .371$, $P < .01$).

Ratings of voice attractiveness by same- and opposite-sex raters were also calculated. Opposite-sex voice ratings were comparable to same-sex ratings. There were significant correlations between male ratings of female voices and female same-sex voice attractiveness ratings ($r=.732$, $n=46$, $P<.01$) and between female ratings of male voices and male same-sex voice attractiveness ratings ($r=.650$, $n=50$, $P<.01$). Therefore, same- and opposite-sex ratings were pooled for certain analyses.

3. Results

Each of the seven bilateral traits was measured twice to achieve a more stable estimate and this also enabled us to check the measurements for reliability. Correlations between the two repeated measurements for each trait were high and ranged from $r=.941$ to $r=.988$.

A Pearson Product–Moment Correlation revealed that voice attractiveness scores and the overall FA index were inversely proportional to one another ($r=-.460$, $n=96$, $P<.01$). Thus, as shown in Fig. 1, as the degree of morphological asymmetry increased, voice attractiveness decreased.

For females, the overall FA index was negatively correlated with both opposite-sex voice attractiveness ratings ($r=-.408$, $n=46$, $P<.01$) and same-sex voice attractiveness ratings

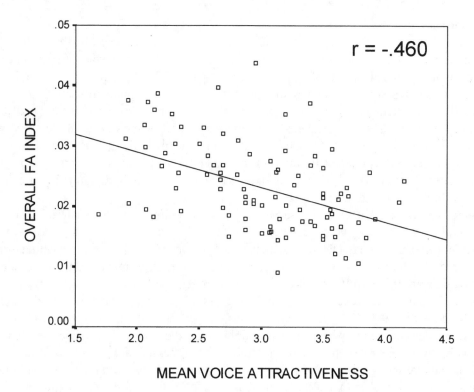

Fig. 1. Scatter plot showing the relationship between overall FA index and ratings of voice attractiveness.

($r = -.597$, $n = 46$, $P < .01$). For males, the overall FA index was also negatively correlated with both opposite-sex voice attractiveness ratings ($r = -.364$, $n = 50$, $P < .01$) and same-sex voice attractiveness ratings ($r = -.412$, $n = 50$, $P < .01$).

Correlations between the FA of individual traits and voice attractiveness ratings were also computed and the results are included in the correlation matrix presented in Table 1. Without exception, all of the correlations between the FA of individual traits and voice attractiveness were negative (binomial test, $P = .016$). Thus, as deviations from bilateral symmetry increased, voice attractiveness ratings decreased. Significant negative correlations ($P < .01$) with voice attractiveness were obtained for the second ($r = -.310$), fourth ($r = -.309$), and fifth digit ($r = -.277$) digit length asymmetries. The overall FA index, however, was a better predictor of voice ratings ($r = -.460$) than any of the individual traits. The overall FA index not only accounted for more of the variance in voice attractiveness but, as shown in Table 1, the overall FA index was significantly correlated with all of the seven traits (correlations ranged from $r = .310$ to $r = .477$).

The ratio of the length of the second digit to the fourth digit was also calculated for both males and females. Averaged across both hands, second digit/fourth digit ratios did not correlate significantly with voice attractiveness ratings for either males ($r = .162$) or females ($r = -.007$).

4. Discussion

Whereas digit length ratios and voice were not related, ratings of voice attractiveness did covary with independent morphological measures of bilateral symmetry. Since bilateral symmetry appears to be a phenotypic marker of viability, fecundity, and health (see Thornhill & Møller, 1997), voice may also serve as an index of genetic quality. The asymmetries of the traits we measured are very subtle, and would not usually be obvious as a means of assessing potential mates. On the other hand, individual differences in vocal quality can be easily detected and assessed. Thus, if bilateral symmetry and voice attractiveness covary, voice may be a more salient marker of underlying genetic quality and viability as it relates to mate choice.

There is evidence that voice is used as a cue for assessing potential mates. For instance, individuals with attractive voices are perceived more favorably and are judged to have more desirable personality characteristics (Zuckerman & Driver, 1989). People with attractive voices are also thought to be warmer, more likable, honest, dominant, and more likely to succeed than are those with less attractive voices (Berry, 1990; Zuckerman & Driver, 1989). Thus, a "vocal attractiveness stereotype" appears to exist (Zuckerman & Driver, 1989; Zuckerman et al., 1990). Favorable impressions of speakers with attractive voices have been obtained under conditions where observers only heard the speaker's voice, as well as when they both saw and heard the speaker. Furthermore, the higher the rating of vocal attractiveness, the more similar the speaker is judged to be to the rater and the more the rater would like to affiliate with the speaker (Miyake & Zuckerman, 1993). In addition to making personality inferences based on voice, inferences about physical features are not uncommon. For example, although they are not always accurate, women assess men with voices of closely spaced, low-frequency harmonics to be more attractive, older, heavier, and more likely to have masculine features, such as a hairy chest and muscular body (Collins, 2000).

Our data suggest that voice may provide information about fitness. Just as symmetrical individuals are judged as more attractive in terms of their appearance (Grammer & Thornhill, 1994; Mealey, Bridgstock, & Townsend, 1999), so are their voices. Thus, bilaterally symmetrical traits may not only affect appearance, but early developmental instabilities may also impact perception and interpersonal attraction in the auditory domain. Unlike assessing physical attractiveness based on visual cues, voice assessments are light independent (Gallup & Cameron, 1992). This may have been especially important during human evolution prior to the invention of artificial illumination. Social interactions that occurred after dark under conditions of polygamous mating strategies could have had important reproductive implications. Moreover, because hominids tend to be nocturnal copulators (Ford & Beach, 1951), there may have been added emphasis placed on voice as a means of mate assessment/selection.

References

Berry, D. (1990). Vocal attractiveness and vocal babyishness: effects on stranger, self and friend impressions. *Journal of Nonverbal Behavior, 14*, 141–153.

Collins, S. A. (2000). Men's voices and women's choices. *Animal Behaviour, 60*, 773–780.

Ford, C. S., & Beach, F. A. (1951). *Patterns of sexual behavior*. New York: Harper & Bros. and Paul B. Hoeber.

Gallup Jr., G. G., & Cameron, P. A. (1992). Modality specific metaphors: is our mental machinery "colored" by a visual bias? *Metaphor and Symbolic Activity, 7*, 93–98.

Gangestad, S. W., & Thornhill, R. (1997). The evolutionary psychology of extrapair sex: the role of fluctuating asymmetry. *Evolution and Human Behavior, 18*, 69–88.

Gangestad, S. W., & Thornhill, R. (1998). Menstrual cycle variation in women's preferences for the scent of symmetrical men. *Proceedings of the Royal Society of London, 265*, 927–933.

Gangestad, S. W., Thornhill, R., & Yeo, R. A. (1994). Facial attractiveness, developmental stability, fluctuating asymmetry. *Ethology and Sociobiology, 15*, 73–85.

Grammer, K., & Thornhill, R. (1994). Human (*Homo sapiens*) facial attractiveness and sexual selection: the role of symmetry and averageness. *Journal of Comparative Psychology, 108*, 233–242.

Livshits, G., & Kobyliansky, E. (1991). Fluctuating asymmetry as a possible measure of developmental homeostasis in humans: a review. *Human Biology, 63*, 441–466.

Manning, J. T., Barley, L., Walton, J., Lewis-Jones, D. I., Trivers, R. L., Singh, D., Thornhill, R., Rohde, P., Bereczkei, T., Henzi, P., Soler, M., & Szwed, A. (2000). The 2nd:4th digit ratio, sexual dimorphism, population differences, reproductive success: evidence for sexually antagonistic genes? *Evolution and Human Behavior, 21*, 163–183.

Manning, J. T., Koukourakis, K., & Brodie, D. A. (1997). Fluctuating asymmetry, metabolic rate and sexual selection in human males. *Evolution and Human Behavior, 18*, 15–21.

Manning, J. T., Scutt, D., Whitehouse, G. H., & Leinster, S. J. (1997). Breast asymmetry and phenotypic quality in women. *Evolution and Human Behavior, 18*, 223–236.

Martin, S. M., Manning, J. T., & Dowrick, C. F. (1999). Fluctuating asymmetry, relative digit length, depression in men. *Evolution and Human Behavior, 20*, 203–214.

Mealey, L., Bridgstock, R., & Townsend, G. C. (1999). Symmetry and perceived facial attractiveness: a monozygotic co-twin comparison. *Journal of Personality and Social Psychology, 76*, 151–158.

Miyake, K., & Zuckerman, M. (1993). Beyond personality impressions: effects of physical and vocal attractiveness on false consensus, social comparison, affiliation, assumed and perceived similarity. *Journal of Personality, 61*, 411–437.

Møller, A. P., Soler, M., & Thornhill, R. (1995). Breast asymmetry, sexual selection, human reproductive success. *Evolution and Human Behavior, 16*, 207–219.

Perrett, D. I., Burt, D. M., Penton-Voak, I. S., Lee, K. J., Rowland, D. A., & Edwards, R. (1999). Symmetry and human facial attractiveness. *Evolution and Human Behavior, 20*, 295–307.

Scutt, D., Manning, J. T., Whitehouse, G. H., Leinster, S. J., & Massey, C. P. (1997). The relationship between breast asymmetry, breast size and occurrence of breast cancer. *British Journal of Radiology, 70*, 1017–1021.

Thornhill, R., Gangestad, S., & Comer, R. (1995). Human female orgasm and mate fluctuating asymmetry. *Animal Behaviour, 50*, 1601–1615.

Thornhill, R., & Gangestad, S. W. (1994). Human fluctuating asymmetry and sexual behavior. *Psychological Science, 5*, 297–302.

Thornhill, R., & Gangestad, S. W. (1999). The scent of symmetry: a human sex pheromone that signals fitness? *Evolution and Human Behavior, 20*, 175–201.

Thornhill, R., & Møller, A. P. (1997). Developmental stability, disease and medicine. *Biological Reviews, 72*, 497–548.

Wedekind, C., & Furi, S. (1997). Body odour preference in men and women: do they aim for specific MHC combinations or simply heterozygosity? *Proceedings of the Royal Society of London, 264*, 1471–1479.

Zuckerman, M., & Driver, R. (1989). What sounds beautiful is good: the vocal attractiveness stereotype. *Journal of Nonverbal Behavior, 13*, 67–82.

Zuckerman, M., Hodgins, H., & Miyake, K. (1990). The vocal attractiveness stereotype: replication and elaboration. *Journal of Nonverbal Behavior, 14*, 97–112.

ELSEVIER

Evolution and Human Behavior 23 (2002) 181–192

Evolution
and Human
Behavior

Testosterone, cortisol, and women's competition

Helen S. Bateup[a], Alan Booth[b],*, Elizabeth A. Shirtcliff[c],
Douglas A. Granger[c]

[a]*The Laboratory of Neuroendocrinology, The RockSeller University, New York, NY 10021*
[b]*Sociology Department, Pennsylvania State University, 511 Oswald Tower, University Park, PA 16802, USA*
[c]*Department of Biobehavioral Health, Pennsylvania State University, University Park, PA 16802, USA*

Received 5 September 2001; received in revised form 17 November 2001; accepted 20 November 2001

Abstract

Hormone (testosterone, cortisol)–behavior relationships have been extensively studied among male competitors, and far less so among female competitors. To address this gap, we studied members of a nationally recognized college women's rugby team. Seventeen players (ages 18–22 years) provided saliva samples 24 h before, 20 min prior to, and immediately after five league matches. Subjects self-reported aggressiveness, team bonding, pregame mental state, postgame performance evaluation, and whether the opponent was more or less challenging than expected. Results revealed that both testosterone and cortisol levels increased in anticipation of the matches. Postgame levels of both hormones were higher than pregame levels. The pregame rise in testosterone was associated with team bonding, aggressiveness, and being focused, but was unrelated to perceptions of the opponent's skill. Testosterone change during the game was unrelated to winning or losing, evaluations of personal performance, or perceptions of the opponent's threat. Game changes in cortisol were positively related to player evaluations of whether the opponent was more of a challenge than expected, and negatively related to losing. These results are compared with hormone–behavior patterns found among male competitors and are interpreted within a recent theory of sex differences in response to challenges. © 2002 Elsevier Science Inc. All rights reserved.

Keywords: Women competitors; Competition and hormones; Testosterone; Cortisol

* Corresponding author. Tel.: +1-814-863-1141; fax: +1-814-863-7216.
E-mail address: axb24@psu.edu (A. Booth).

1090-5138/02/$ – see front matter © 2002 Elsevier Science Inc. All rights reserved.
PII: S1090-5138(01)00100-3

1. Introduction

This study examined temporal hormonal responses to aggressive competition in elite college women athletes. An extensive body of research has focused on hormonal responses to competition, but the subjects are nearly always male. Few studies have explored parallel relationships in women. This study furthers our understanding of the degree to which women's hormones change in anticipation of and response to aggressive competition, and how hormones are related to performance, cognition, and attitudes among women competitors. Findings permit indirect comparison of hormone–behavior links in female competitors with the patterns found in research on males.

The role of testosterone and cortisol in male competitors has attracted substantial attention from behavioral endocrinologists who have studied tennis, wrestling, basketball, and chess, as well as competitive tasks in laboratory settings. The only carefully controlled study of women's competition to date focused on women and men competing with same-sex partners in a video game (Mazur, Susman, & Edelbrock, 1997). The present study of women's rugby is an ideal parallel to the many male studies. Women's rugby requires the physical contact and tackling that are characteristic of American football, yet without the protective equipment. Two teams of 15 players compete against each other. To forward the ball, players run, pass, or kick for 80 min with no time-outs. The opposing team defends by tackling the ball carriers and attempting to drive the ball to their side. All players are involved in tackling, driving, running, and passing. In this forum, active physical domination by women players is required and rewarded. This is one of the rare natural social ecologies in which women's hormonal responses to highly physical aggressive competition can be studied.

1.1. Male competition

1.1.1. Testosterone

In men, the relationship between testosterone and competition is reciprocal. Males characteristically experience a testosterone increase in anticipation of competition (Booth, Shelly, Mazur, Tharp, & Kittok, 1989). The precompetition rise is likely to make the individual more willing to take risks (Daltzman & Zuckerman, 1980), improve psychomotor function and coordination (Herrmann & Beach, 1976), and increase cognitive performance (Herrmann, McDonald, & Bozak, 1976; Klaiber, Broverman, Vogel, Abraham, & Cone, 1971; Vogel, Broverman, Klaiber, Abraham, & Cone, 1971). For a few hours following competition, testosterone is high for winners relative to losers (Booth et al., 1989; Elias, 1981; Mazur & Lamb, 1980). The rise in testosterone following a win is associated with positive mood (Booth et al., 1989), and is thought to be important because winners often face challenges from others soon after gaining new status. There are exceptions to this general finding. Two studies found no difference in testosterone levels between winners and losers (Gonzalez-Bono, Salvador, Serrano, & Ricart, 1999; Salvadore, Simon, Suay, & Llorens, 1987) and one found losers to have higher levels than winners (Filaire, Masso, Sagnol, Lac, & Ferrand, 2001).

Both the pregame rise and the response to winning or losing are less likely to occur if the individual regards the event as unimportant, if he feels certain that he will win or lose because the opponent has a very different level of skill (Mazur, Booth, & Dabbs, 1992; Mazur & Lamb, 1980; Salvadore et al., 1987), or if he believes the outcome was due to luck or a referee's decision (Gonzalez-Bono et al., 1999). Studies show that these changes also occur in nonphysical competition such as chess matches (Mazur et al., 1992) and contests in reaction time (Gladue, Boechler, & McCaul, 1989). Indeed, active participation in the competition is not necessarily required: testosterone levels increase among spectators watching their favorite sports teams win and decrease for fans of the losing teams (Bernhardt, Dabbs, Fielden, & Lutter, 1989). These findings suggest that the link between competition and testosterone in males operates in a wide variety of competitive situations but is highly contingent on perceptions that gain or loss of status is at stake.

1.1.2. Cortisol

Information about the role of cortisol in competition is not as comprehensive. Some studies suggest that cortisol may play a role in behaviors important in competition, including aggression, arousal, and mobilization of physiological resources to deal with impending threat or challenge. There is anticipatory elevation in cortisol in men and a rise during the competitive event (Booth et al., 1989; Elias, 1981). Another aspect of the cortisol–competition link is that top-seeded male tennis players exhibited consistently lower cortisol levels than did less talented players, suggesting that highly successful competitors may have above average ability at managing stress (Booth et al., 1989).

1.2. Female competition

To our knowledge, only one carefully controlled study has examined competition and hormone changes in women. Mazur et al. (1997) obtained saliva samples from 28 men and 32 women before, during, and after competing with same-sex partners in a video game. They found that men's testosterone and cortisol followed the familiar pattern of a pregame rise but that there was no postgame difference in response to winning and losing. Women, on the other hand, experienced no change in testosterone and cortisol production, except for a downward trajectory most likely due to diurnal variation. Overall, women's cortisol level was higher than the men's, which may indicate that they experienced the event as more unfamiliar or challenging than did the men. While this was a carefully controlled study, women seldom play video games, compared to men, and may not have felt that the event challenged their status. The fact that male losers and winners did not differ from one another may also indicate that men did not find the video game sufficiently engaging to invest in the experience as a challenge to their status.

1.3. Interpreting sex differences in hormonal responses to competition

Lack of research notwithstanding, there are reasons to expect differences in the hormone–behavior links between women and men competitors. One reason is that women produce five to seven times less testosterone, a hormone that acts to develop the male brain for aggressive or dominant behavior in many species, than men (Nelson, 2000). Another reason is that while activation of the hypothalamic–pituitary–gonadal axis is the primary source for testosterone in men, in women the majority of testosterone is derived from the peripheral metabolism of dehydroepiandrosterone (DHEA) (Parker, 1991). DHEA is secreted by the adrenal gland in response to activation of the HPA axis in reaction to challenging or threatening events and is associated with changes in cortisol. If HPA activation and subsequent release of DHEA are linked to increases in women's testosterone levels, it is biologically plausible to believe that women have a different pattern of relationships among testosterone, cortisol, and competition than do men.

Still another reason to expect sex differences is that parental investments may predispose women to adopt a different response pattern than men to challenges and stress. Taylor et al. (2000) suggest that women's response to challenges may be more defensive in nature than men's, which they characterize as a "tend-and-befriend" strategy to differentiate it from the "fight-or-flight" response attributed to men. In females, fight may put their offspring in danger, while flight may be compromised by pregnancy or may interfere with offspring care. Tending entails nurturing activities intended to protect and calm offspring and befriending involves creating and maintaining networks that provide resources and protection for self and offspring. As such, Taylor et al. propose that the typical low levels of testosterone in adult females indicate that androgens are unlikely to be the organizing factors that evoke a tend-and-befriend response. We will examine our findings in light of this theory.

The study described here explored several important issues. First, it looked at whether women's testosterone and cortisol show a precompetition rise and, if so, sought to ascertain the source of the increase and if it influenced perceived performance. Second, it investigated whether women's testosterone and cortisol respond to winning and losing or relate to the seriousness of the challenge posed by the opponents. Third, whether top-seeded women (highest ranked athletes) have lower cortisol just prior to the match was examined. Then, a number of issues that have not yet been studied in men were explored. For example, are particular cognitive or emotional experiences associated with precompetition elevations in hormones? How are individual differences in testosterone or cortisol related to social affiliation in the form of team bonding and camaraderie? Do individuals who enjoy the aggressive play and think of themselves as aggressive have higher pregame increases in testosterone?

2. Methods

2.1. Participants

Seventeen members of a university women's rugby team (ages 18–22 years) gave informed consent to participate in the research. The university's Institutional Review Board approved the use of human subjects in this study. All subjects were varsity players who had individually participated in the National Under-23 Tournament or other regional all-star competitions. Participants had played rugby for at least one previous season. They played an average of three games each, although the number ranged from two to five. The reason players did not play in all five games was due to injury or a less than exemplary performance in the last game or two. The unit of analysis was player–games rather than either players or games ($N = 50$). A player–game was defined as a game in which the player competed for the entire 80-min period for which complete behavioral and salivary data were available. We selected player–game as the unit of analysis because estimates of variables vary by both game and player. For data analysis, we combined the players in each game into a single file. While combining the players from each of the five games creates a design effect (for which we correct), we believe the strategy is a sound one because it increases the number of cases, and thus statistical power. Player–games, however, are not independent because a player can generate anywhere from two to five records (one for each game in which they participated); this serves to bias the statistics generated from *t* tests and ordinary least squares regression. To correct for this problem, the coefficients, means, and statistical tests for all analyses were estimated with SVYREG and SVYMEAN procedures in Stata Corp. (1999), which uses first-order Taylor series approximation to estimate accurate standard errors in clustered data. The standard errors estimated with SVYREG and SVYMEAN will fall between the size of the standard errors, assuming the degrees of freedom is the number of independent players and the size assuming that the degrees of freedom is the number of games. (Which is closer depends on the degree of homogeneity within the clusters.) The procedures used in SVYREG and SVYMEAN were created to estimate correct standard errors for a wide range of designs that involved correlated data (Graubard & Korn, 1994).

2.2. Behavioral and attitudinal measures

We derived a four-item scale of *aggressive competitiveness*. Two items asked subjects to rate the degree to which they agreed or disagreed with the following statements: "I play rugby because I enjoy aggressive contact" and "I play rugby because I enjoy competing." One question asked them to indicate the kind of person they were by deciding where they fall on a pair of contradictory characteristics: "very aggressive/not at all aggressive." In another item, players were asked to rate how they felt about contact during the game on a five-point scale, ranging from "I love contact situations/I always look for them during the game" to "I'm very uncomfortable in contact situations/I often avoid them." Appropriate items were reverse-coded so that higher scores represented more aggressiveness. Factor analysis revealed that the items constituted a single dimension with factor loadings of .50 or above. The scale had a Cronbach's α coefficient of .72.

Bonding was assessed from a five-point agree–disagree item that stated "I play rugby because I enjoy having teammates and bonding." Seventy percent of the players strongly agreed with the statement. Those who strongly agreed were coded 1, others, 0.

Potential challenge posed by the opposing team was obtained from the team captain and was based on past performance of the team with respect to other opponents as well as the challenge they posed to the team we studied.

Athlete's skill was marked by player rank and number of seasons played. Player rank was determined by the team captain in consultation with the coach. Higher numbers represented lower rank.

Pregame mental state was obtained from the following questions: "Rate how much the following statements describe your current state. I am focused and concentrating on the match. I am excited and looking forward to playing. I am fearful and anxious about playing." Players scored themselves as follows: 1 = not at all, 2 = a little bit, 3 = somewhat, 4 = quite a bit, and 5 = a lot.

Postgame perception was obtained immediately following the game. The players assessed their performance by responding to the following question: (1) "Regardless of the outcome, how would you rate your performance today compared to what it usually is? A lot better than I usually play, Somewhat better than usual, About the same, Not quite as good, A lot worse than I usually do?" Personal contribution to the game was assessed with the question: "How much do you feel that your play contributed to or caused the outcome of the match? Not very much at all, a little bit, quite a bit, or a lot?" We measured the players' estimate of the challenge created by the opponent during the game on a three-point scale: "Was your opponent as good as you thought they would be? (1) They gave us more of a struggle than we expected, (2) they played at the level we expected, (3) they were not as challenging as we thought they would be."

2.3. Saliva collection and hormone assays

Saliva samples were collected 24 h before ("baseline"), 15 min before, and immediately after five league games. Baseline samples were obtained at the same time of day as the collection of pregame samples. Samples were obtained by having the players chew a piece of sugarless Original Flavor Trident gum and expectorate through a plastic straw into a 20-ml collection vial. Samples were transported on ice to the Penn State Behavioral Endocrinology Laboratory and stored frozen at − 20 °C until assay. On the day of testing, all samples were centrifuged at 3000 rpm for 10 min to remove mucins. The clear sample was pipetted into appropriate testing wells or tubes. Samples were screened for problems with low pH; samples testing outside the pH range of 4–9 were diluted in PBS to correct pH prior to testing (Schwartz, Granger, Susman, Gunnar, & Laird, 1998).

2.3.1. Cortisol (µg/dl)
All samples were assayed for salivary cortisol using a highly sensitive enzyme immuno-assay specifically designed for use with saliva (Salimetrics, University Park, PA). The test uses only 25 µl of saliva (for singlet determinations) and has a lower limit of sensitivity of 0.007 µg/dl, a range of sensitivity from 0.007 to 1.2 µg/dl, and average intra- and interassay coefficients of variation (CVs) of 5.72% and 8.21%, respectively. The standard curve was highly reproducible (mean $r = .999$). Method accuracies, determined by spike recovery, and linearity, determined by serial dilution, were 105% and 95%.

2.3.2. Testosterone (pg/ml)
Samples were assayed for salivary testosterone using a double antibody radioimmunoassay for total serum testosterone, following Granger, Schwartz, Booth, and Arentz (1999). The assay used 200 µl of saliva (for singlet determinations), and had a minimum detection limit of

0.8 pg/ml and maximum of 250 pg/ml. Intra- and interassay CVs were 4.56% and 12.68%, respectively. The standard curve was highly reproducible (mean $r=.992$). Method accuracy, determined by spike recovery, and linearity, determined by serial dilution, were 99.20% and 92.80%, respectively.

2.3.3. Assay quality control and assurance

In each assay, controls representing low and high salivary levels were included. All samples and controls were assayed in duplicate. Samples with duplicate values that varied by more than 5% were subject to repeat testing. The average of the duplicate tests was used in the analyses. Sample values that represented extreme scores were retested using $\times 2$ and $\times 4$ dilutions. All samples from the same players were tested in the same assay batch.

3. Results

3.1. Descriptive analyses of hormone change

To minimize between-subject variation, each subject's raw hormone values were divided by the subject's highest measured level. The percentages of maximum value per individual were used in all analyses. Baseline, pregame, and postgame levels of testosterone and cortisol are shown in Table 1. The t tests were used to assess the statistical significance of hormone change over time. All P values are two-tailed. Testosterone increased 24% from baseline to just prior to the game [$t(49)=-3.811$, $P=.06$]. Over the course of the game, testosterone increased by a further 49% [$t(49)=-7.552$, $P=.002$]. These compare to a pregame rise of 36% and a game rise of 6% among men tennis players (Booth et al., 1989) and a 12% match rise among wrestlers (Elias, 1981). Cortisol went through parallel changes. Pregame cortisol increased 30% [$t(49)=-2.455$, $P=.01$] and change over the course of the game was 51% [$t(49)=-4.444$, $P=.000$]. Comparable changes among male tennis players were 30% and 26%, respectively (Booth et al., 1989); the game rise among wrestlers was 46% (Elias, 1981). The pregame rise for testosterone and cortisol was similar for men and women, whereas the game rises in the two hormones tended to be higher in women than in men. This difference may be rooted in the fact that the primary source of both hormones is the same in women (the adrenal glands), whereas they differ for men. Among women, the process by which exertion and the challenge to status stimulate cortisol release may also increase testosterone

Table 1
Standardized mean hormone levels (computed as a proportion of the particular individual woman's maximum level) for each collection and statistical significance of differences

Hormone	Baseline	Pregame	Postgame	Significance	
				Baseline – pregame	Pregame – postgame
Testosterone	0.41	0.51	0.76	.01	.000
Cortisol	0.33	0.43	0.65	.06	.02

production. The high correlation between cortisol and testosterone production among women during the game supports such an interpretation [$r(49)=.46$, $P=.01$].

3.2. Pregame testosterone and cortisol

Studies of male competitors indicate that a pregame rise in testosterone is related to performance. Among women, we found limited evidence of a link between the pregame rise and performance. The pregame testosterone increase was significantly correlated with reports of being focused just prior to the match [$r(49)=.30$, $P=.03$]. The link between testosterone and focus is consistent with prior studies as reported by Dabbs and Dabbs (2000, p. 45). Unlike men, the pregame testosterone increase among women was unrelated to perceptions of how easy or difficult the opponent was thought to be prior to the game.

Another way in which the rugby players differed from male competitors was that cortisol levels just prior to the game were unrelated to the rank or experience of the player. The more talented rugby players were just as stressed as less-talented teammates, suggesting that females may be more collective than individualistic in their expression of aggression.

We then examined the player trait-like qualities of aggressive competitiveness and team bonding on the pregame rise in testosterone. Aggressiveness did not have a statistically significant direct relationship with the pregame rise in testosterone but bonding did [$r(46)=.38$, $P=.05$]. However, when both were entered in an ordinary least squares equation, bonding's relationship to the pregame rise continued ($\beta=.44$, $P=.05$) and aggression obtained a marginally significant relationship ($\beta=.28$, $P=.07$). The combined effect of bonding and aggression is shown in Fig. 1. Among those who are motivated to play rugby because they enjoy having teammates and bonding, those who perceived themselves as highly aggressive experienced a much greater increase in precompetition testosterone than those who liked the bonding but were moderately aggressive and those who were not motivated by bonding.

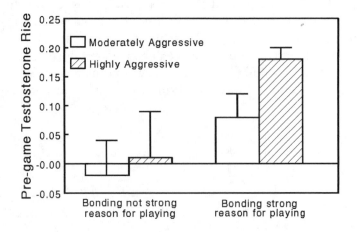

Fig. 1. Bonding, aggression, and pregame testosterone rise.

3.3. Testosterone and cortisol during the game

The increase in women's testosterone in response to a game was unrelated to winning or losing or to the evaluation of personal performance. Two factors were related to the cortisol rise during the game: (1) the extent to which the opposing team was more challenging than expected (something not studied in men) and (2) whether the team won or lost. Players who reported the opponent to be more challenging than expected experienced a mean rise in cortisol of 46 percentage points. When the opponent played at the level of skill expected, cortisol rose by 26 percentage points, whereas it increased by only 8 percentage points when the opponent was not as challenging as expected. In short, the greater the challenge experienced by the players during the game, the greater the increase in cortisol levels $[F(49)=4.378, P=.04]$. When the team lost, cortisol levels rose 0.34 µg/dl, whereas they only increased by 0.14 µg/dl if they won $[F(49)=3.973, P=.03]$. The latter finding differs from those in studies of men. Elias (1981) found that, compared to losers, winners' cortisol increased. Booth et al. (1989) found no relationship between cortisol change during the game and winning and losing.

4. Conclusion and discussion

The study explored relationships between testosterone and cortisol production in anticipation of and response to aggressive and physical competition among women. Because the context of rugby is similar to that of sports used in many studies of male competition, it provides a, heretofore, unique opportunity to compare the role of hormones in women's and men's competition. Such comparisons are important because although much is known about the role of hormones in male competitors (relative to female competitors), there are important sex differences in hormone production and perhaps in biobehavioral responses to stress and challenges.

In contrast to Mazur et al. (1997) who found no similarities between the sexes with respect to hormone production and competition, we found both similarities and differences. Perhaps the testosterone changes we observed would not occur in the types of competition studied by Mazur et al., in which individuals, rather than teams, took part in a game that involved motor skills and few physical demands. Studies of female competitors in low and high physically challenging competition and in team and individual sports are needed to resolve the differences between the two studies.

One also has to consider whether female rugby players, because of the demands of the sport, are self-selected in a way that differs from women competitors in other sports. While we do not have other female competitors with whom to conduct a comparison, we did have the opportunity to compare rugby players' baseline testosterone level with that for a group of married women in their 30s who are part of another study. Twenty-one provided samples in the early afternoon — roughly the same time rugby matches were held. The mean 24-h pregame testosterone level was 13.2 µg/dl; for the 21 women, it was 12.1 µg/dl. The small difference could well be due to the fact that the rugby players exercised much more than the other women.

This is consistent with studies showing that exercise stimulates testosterone production (Mazur, 1998). Thus, on the basis of testosterone production, it would appear that rugby players in this study do not differ appreciably from other women.

How are the links between hormones and competition similar and different for men and women, and what can be said about the differences? There is a similarity in that both men and women experience an anticipatory rise in testosterone that is related to performance. They differ, however, in that men's rise is tempered by the magnitude of the threat posed by the opponent— anticipating a challenge from an opponent of comparable skill leads to a larger rise than one from a much weaker or much stronger opponent. Men and women also share a precompetition rise in cortisol, but its bearing on performance is unclear. There are several differences. For one, men's pregame cortisol is related to skill and experience—more talented competitors have lower cortisol (perhaps related to more effective stress management) than less-skilled men, something not found in women. Furthermore, men and women differ in their hormonal response to winning and losing. Many, but not all, male winners experience an increase in testosterone (correlated with elevation in positive evaluations of performance), while losers show a decline in the hormone. While women experience a rise in testosterone during competition that is greater than men's, it is unrelated to either self-evaluation of performance, or winning and losing. On the other hand, changes in cortisol are related to the outcome of the contest: female winners have lower cortisol than do losers, something that does not occur among men.

To what extent do these differences support or challenge the "tend-and-befriend" hypothesis? The "tend-and-befriend" model proposes that androgens are less involved in organizing the response to women's challenges. Yet, the pregame rise in testosterone is very similar to that of men, which is not consistent with the hypothesis. On the other hand, two findings—that women's pregame rise testosterone was not influenced by the magnitude of the threat posed by the challenger, and that pregame cortisol was unrelated to the skill of the player—are consistent with the hypothesis. The "tend-and-befriend" model suggests that oxytocin regulates women's hormone response to threats. Without oxytocin data, however, we cannot evaluate this possibility. Future studies that include oxytocin are warranted.

Also of interest is the observation that following a win the rugby players did not experience the testosterone-related elevation in positive evaluations of performance often observed in male competitors. Nor did the losers experience the decline in testosterone experienced by men. Rather, women who won experienced a very modest increase in cortisol compared to a relatively large increase among those who lost. These findings are consistent with Taylor et al. (2000) suggestion that females' responses to challenges are more likely to be directed toward creating and maintaining relationships. Competition, especially that which is physically aggressive, has the potential to threaten old relationships and prevent the creation of new ones. Lower cortisol associated with winning suggests that females are managing the challenge of competition effectively so that high cortisol levels do not interfere with the conciliatory behavior that restores potentially beneficial relationships with individuals who were opponents a few moments earlier and teammates who were challenged in the heat of the competition. These women may very well be on the same team in all-star games; under such circumstances, they could not carry over animosity from earlier games in which they had been opponents.

The role of team bonding as an influence on the pregame rise in testosterone is important, as is its role in enhancing the influence of trait aggression on testosterone production. To our knowledge, this is the first time anyone has identified bonding as being at the root of the anticipatory rise in testosterone. Determining whether bonding plays the same role among male competitors is of considerable interest. A negative finding would support the part of the tend-and-befriend theory suggesting that aggression tends to be expressed collectively among women compared to men. Overall, we can conclude that the results provide only partial and conditional support for the tend-and-befriend hypothesis.

It is possible that team participation rather than sex differences in biobehavioral response to stress are the key to understanding our results. It is important to keep in mind that the majority of hormone–competition studies involve sports that stress individual performance (e.g., tennis, judo, wrestling, racket ball, chess) more than team efforts. In a team, an individual's status may be more strongly tied to the social interaction within the group than to the outcome of a particular contest. One-on-one competition may have a more direct impact on individual status and, therefore, on the testosterone response to winning and losing. Further studies of team sports will clarify this caveat.

The present study advances our knowledge concerning the role of hormones in competition in several ways. First, it is the first study of women's competition in a team setting. Second, it reveals both similarities and differences in the role played by hormones in men's and women's responses to gaining and losing status. Third, it is the first study to link team spirit and bonding to testosterone production, and especially the way in which bonding enhances the link between trait aggression and testosterone. Fourth, the study generated data that may be used to analyze the way in which hormones are implicated in competing models depicting human response to challenges—fight-or-flight and tend-and-befriend. Fifth, the findings help define questions to be addressed in future research on sex similarities and differences in competition.

Acknowledgments

We thank the outstanding young women athletes who participated in this study for their enthusiastic contribution. We also thank Laura Cousino Klein for feedback on an earlier draft of this manuscript and commentary on the "tend-and-befriend" theory and David R. Johnson for advice on methodological issues. The staff of the Penn State Behavioral Endocrinology Laboratory and the Population Research Institute (which receives core support from NICHD Grant 1-HD28263) deserve recognition for their support. The project was funded by a donation from Dr. and Ms. Evan G. Pattishall, Jr., to Douglas A Granger.

References

Bernhardt, P., Dabbs, J., Fielden, J., & Lutter, C. (1989). Testosterone changes during vicarious experiences of winning and losing among fans at sporting events. *Physiology & Behavior, 65,* 59–62.

Booth, A., Shelly, G., Mazur, A., Tharp, G., & Kittok, R. (1989). Testosterone, and winning and losing in human competition. *Hormones and Behavior*, *23*, 556–571.

Dabbs, J., & Dabbs, M. (2000). *Heros, rogues, and lovers: testosterone and behavior*. New York: McGraw-Hill.

Daltzman, R., & Zuckerman, M. (1980). Disinhibitory sensation seeking, personality and gonadal hormones. *Personality and Individual Differences*, *1*, 103–110.

Elias, M. (1981). Serum cortisol, testosterone, and testosterone-binding globulin responses to competitive fighting in human males. *Aggressive Behavior*, *7*, 215–224.

Filaire, E., Masso, F., Sagnol, M., Lac, G., & Ferrand, S. (2001). Anxiety, hormonal responses and coping during judo competition. *Aggressive Behavior*, *27*, 55–63.

Gladue, B., Boechler, M., & McCaul, K. (1989). Hormonal response to competition in human males. *Aggressive Behavior*, *15*, 409–422.

Gonzalez-Bono, E., Salvador, A., Serrano, M., & Ricart, J. (1998). Testosterone, cortisol and mood in a sports team competition. *Hormones and Behavior*, *35*, 55–62.

Granger, D., Schwartz, E., Booth, A., & Arentz, M. (1999). Salivary testosterone determination in studies of child health and development. *Hormones and Behavior*, *35*, 8–27.

Graubard, B. I., & Korn, E. L. (1994). Regression analysis with cluster data. *Statistics and Medicine*, *13*, 509–522.

Herrmann, W., & Beach, R. (1976). Psychotropic effects of androgens: a review of clinical observations and new human experimental findings. *Pharmakopsychiatrie/Neuro-Psychopharmakologie*, *9*, 205–219.

Herrmann, W., McDonald, R., & Bozak, M. (1976). A psycho experimental model for the investigation of hormones as psychotropic agents. In: T. Itil, G. Laudahn, & W. Herrmann (Eds.), *The psychotropic effects of hormones* (pp. 79–120). New York: Spectrum.

Klaiber, L., Broverman, D., Vogel, W., Abraham, G., & Cone, F. (1971). Effects of infused testosterone on mental performances and serum LH. *Journal of Clinical Endocrinology and Metabolism*, *32*, 341–349.

Mazur, A. (1998). Aging and testosterone. *Science*, *279*, 305–306.

Mazur, A., Booth, A., & Dabbs, J. (1992). Testosterone and chess competition. *Social Psychology Quarterly*, *55*, 70–77.

Mazur, A., & Lamb, T. (1980). Testosterone status, and mood in human males. *Hormones and Behavior*, *14*, 236–246.

Mazur, A., Susman, E., & Edelbrock, S. (1997). Sex differences in testosterone response to a video game contest. *Evolution and Human Behavior*, *18*, 317–326.

Nelson, R. (2000). *An introduction to behavioral endocrinology*. Sunderland, MA: Sinauer Associates.

Parker, L. N. (1991). Adrenarche. *Endocrinology and Metabolism Clinics of North America*, *20*, 71–83.

Salvadore, A., Simon, V., Suay, F., & Llorens, L. (1987). Testosterone and cortisol responses to competitive fighting in human males. *Aggressive Behavior*, *13*, 9–13.

Schwartz, E., Granger, D. A., Susman, E. J., Gunnar, M., & Laird, B. (1998). Assessing salivary cortisol in studies of child development. *Child Development*, *69*, 1503–1513.

Stata Corp. (1999). *Stata Statistical Software: Release 6.0*. College Station, TX: Stata Corporation.

Taylor, S., Klein, L., Lewis, B., Gruenewald, T., Gurung, R., & Updegaff, J. (2000). Biobehavioral responses to stress in females: tend-and-befriend, not fight-or-flight. *Psychological Review*, *107*, 411–429.

Vogel, M., Broverman, E., Klaiber, E., Abraham, G., & Cone, F. (1971). Effects of testosterone infusions upon EEG's of normal male adults. *Electroencephalography and Clinical Neurophysiology*, *31*, 400–403.

ELSEVIER

Evolution and Human Behavior 23 (2002) 193–201

Evolution
and Human
Behavior

Marriage and fatherhood are associated with lower testosterone in males

Peter B. Gray*, Sonya M. Kahlenberg, Emily S. Barrett,
Susan F. Lipson, Peter T. Ellison

Department of Anthropology, Harvard University, 11 Divinity Avenue, Cambridge, MA 02138, USA

Received 24 October 2000; received in revised form 8 November 2001; accepted 7 December 2001

Abstract

In order to study the hormonal correlates of the tradeoff between mating and parenting effort in human males, we examined the salivary testosterone (T) levels of 58 Boston-area men who were either unmarried ($n = 29$), married without children ($n = 14$), or married with children ($n = 15$). Additionally, we asked participants to complete a questionnaire that surveyed their demographic, marital, and parenting backgrounds. We tested the hypotheses that (1) T levels will be lower in married than in unmarried men and (2) married men with children will have lower T levels than unmarried men and married men without children. We also tested a series of hypotheses relating variation in parenting and spousal relationships to T. We found that married men with and without children had significantly lower evening T than unmarried men. No significant differences in T were found among the groups in morning samples. Among married men without children, higher scores on a "spousal investment" measure and more hours spent with a man's wife on his last day off work were both associated with lower T levels. We suggest that lower T levels during the day among fathers may facilitate paternal care in humans by decreasing the likelihood that a father will engage in competitive and/or mating behavior. © 2002 Elsevier Science Inc. All rights reserved.

Keywords: Testosterone; Marriage; Fatherhood; Paternal care; Mating effort; Parenting effort; Challenge hypothesis

* Corresponding author.
E-mail address: gray@fas.harvard.edu (P.B. Gray).

1090-5138/02/$ – see front matter © 2002 Elsevier Science Inc. All rights reserved.
PII: S 1 0 9 0 - 5 1 3 8 (0 1) 0 0 1 0 1 - 5

1. Introduction

One of the fundamental features of human male life histories involves the tradeoff between the time and energy that individuals allocate to male–male competition and mate attraction (mating effort) and the time and energy they allocate to caring for their mates and offspring (parenting effort) (Lancaster & Kaplan, 1992). In humans, the existence of this tradeoff may account, in part, for the variation in male mating and parenting effort found across (e.g., Flinn & Low, 1986; Hewlett, 1992; Marlowe, 2000) and within (Chisholm, 1999; Draper & Harpending, 1982) societies and across an individual's life span (Daly & Wilson, 1988).

Research on nonhuman taxa has pointed to the steroid hormone testosterone (T) as a key physiological mechanism underlying the mating/parenting tradeoff in males. Wingfield, Hegner, Dufty, and Ball's (1990) "challenge hypothesis" suggests that T facilitates male–male competition in reproductive contexts and conversely is down-regulated during parental care. Evidence supporting the challenge hypothesis stems from work on monogamous bird species, which show high male T levels during mate procurement and then lowered T levels after males pair with their mates and begin caring for their young (Wingfield et al., 1990). Male T levels remain constant throughout the breeding season in polygynous bird species, coinciding with a lack of male parental effort (Wingfield et al., 1990). Similarly, studies with other species have found that T levels are positively associated with behaviors characterized as mating effort (Creel, Creel, Mills, & Monfort, 1997) and negatively associated with those indicative of parenting effort (Ball, 1991; Wynne-Edwards, 2001; Ziegler, 2000). Experimental manipulations have demonstrated a causal role of T, whereby elevations in T are associated with increased mating effort and reduced parenting effort (Ketterson & Nolan, 1999).

In contrast to the endocrine data from other species, surprisingly little is known about the hormonal correlates associated with the tradeoff between mating and parenting effort in human males. Although no study to date has explicitly tested the challenge hypothesis in humans, there are several existing studies that support the view that T may mediate mating and parenting behavior. In their study of over 4000 servicemen, Booth and Dabbs (1993) found that those with higher T were less likely to have ever married and, if they did marry, they were more likely to have engaged in extramarital sex. Mazur and Michalek (1998) reported that in their sample of married men, T levels were highest around 8 and 4 years prior to marriage and began to decline shortly after marriage. They also showed that men who divorced their spouses experienced elevated T around the time of relationship dissolution. Neither of these studies, however, reported the parental status of their married participants, thereby precluding any analysis of the relationship between T and a tradeoff between male mating and parenting effort. Two recent studies have investigated hormonal changes in expectant and new fathers. Storey, Walsh, Quinton, and Wynne-Edwards (2000) found 33% lower T levels among men whose wives had given birth within the previous 3 weeks compared with men whose wives were due to give birth in 3 weeks or less. They also found that parenting stimuli, such as holding a baby doll, decreased T in these men. Similarly, Berg and Wynne-Edwards (2001) reported that salivary T levels were lower for men expecting the birth of their first child than for controls.

Here we present new data, which address the hypothesis that, as in other species, T is associated with a mating/parenting tradeoff in human males. We predicted that: (1) T levels would be lower in married men than in unmarried men and (2) T levels would be lowest in men with children. We also predicted that (3) marriage duration and a measure of male spousal investment would be negatively correlated with T levels among married men without children because marriage duration and higher levels of spousal investment may correspond with lower mating effort. Furthermore, we predicted that (4) the age of a male's youngest child would be positively correlated with T levels, and a measure of male parental investment would be negatively correlated with T levels. These last expectations arise because more invested fathers, as well as fathers of younger children, may provide higher levels of paternal care.

2. Methods

Fifty-eight Boston-area men voluntarily participated in this study (unmarried men, $n = 29$; married men without children, $n = 14$; married men with children, $n = 15$). Of these men, 48 were graduate, professional, or postdoctoral students affiliated with Harvard University. The men ranged in age from 20 to 41 years (mean age = 29.6 years). Unmarried participants were not involved in committed relationships (defined as a relationship with the same partner lasting longer than 3 months). All married subjects were in first marriages, and all fathers in the study had biological children between 1 week and 4 years of age. Four fathers had more than one child.

To test our predictions, we administered a questionnaire that surveyed the demographic, marital, and parenting backgrounds of participants. The questionnaire also contained a stress inventory (Cohen, Tamarck, & Mermelstein, 1983). Items adapted from Lund (1985) were used to generate a composite "spousal investment" measure, and results of five items were compiled to yield a "male parenting effort" measure (see Table 1). Amount of time spent with spouse on a subject's last day off work was converted to a scale of 1 to 5. Self-reported weekly amounts of exercise were placed on a scale of 1 to 5, and heights and weights were used to determine body mass index (BMI). We included these additional variables because they can be associated with variation in T levels (Campbell & Leslie, 1995; Vermeulen, Goemaere, & Kaufman, 1999).

Additionally, we asked participants to collect four saliva samples (two a.m. samples and two p.m. samples). Samples were collected by the subjects at home, following previously validated protocols (Lipson & Ellison, 1989). Saliva was collected using sugarless chewing gum (to stimulate saliva production) into polystyrene tubes pretreated with sodium azide (a preservative), and was stored by the subjects at ambient temperature until all four samples were obtained. Samples were frozen at $-20\,^{\circ}$C until they were assayed. Only morning samples collected between 0600 and 1100 and evening samples collected between 1700 and 2400 were included in the analysis. Participants were instructed to refrain from eating, drinking, smoking, and sexual activity before collecting saliva samples.

Table 1
Items used to generate "spousal investment" and "male parenting" effort scales

	Spousal investment scale (items adapted from Lund, 1985)
1	Spending your free time with your partner rather than doing things or seeing other people.
2	Spending continuous time along together such as evenings together, weekend outings, or vacations.
3	Buying gifts for your partner.
4	Sharing important personal feelings, problems, and beliefs with your partner.
5	Revealing your sexual preferences with your partner.
6	Exploring sexual activities with your partner.
7	Sharing income and expenses with your partner, such as having a joint bank account and debts.
8	Contributing financially to your partner or your relationship in general.
9	Trying to develop interests and activities in common with your partner.
10	Making plans for the future such as discussing having children.
11	Telling your partner your true feelings about the relationship such as that you love her.
12	Letting friends know your feelings and plans about your relationship.
13	Integrating your partner into your family.
14	Putting effort into seeing your partner (such as travelling long distances or travelling often).
15	Doing favors for or helping your partner (such as lending money or doing errands).
16	Changing things about yourself to please your partner such as habits, attitudes, or appearance.
17	Restricting your relationships with other potential partners such as being sexually faithful.
18	Changing your career plans or other interests to continue your marriage.
19	Putting effort into 'making the marriage work' when there were problems.
20	Trying to encourage and support your partner.
21	Investing emotionally in your partner in general.
Scoring system	Each of the 21 items scored on a scale from 1 (*extremely small investment*) to 7 (*extremely large investment*), with the total score (possible range = 21 – 147) determined by adding positive scores of all items.
	"Male parenting effort" scale
1	During your last day off, approximately what percentage of the direct childcare (e.g., bathing, feeding, changing diapers, dressing, etc.) did you do?
2	During your last day off, approximately what percentage of your waking hours was spent doing these direct child care activities?
3	During a normal working day, approximately what percentage of your waking hours is spent doing these direct child care activities?
4	During your last day off, approximately what percentage of your waking hours was spent engaged in "playtime" activities (i.e., reading books, playing with toys, watching cartoons, etc.) with your child(ren)?
5	During a normal working day, approximately what percentage of your waking hours is spent engaged in "playtime" activities (i.e., reading books, playing with toys, watching cartoons, etc.) with your child(ren)?
Scoring system	Answers given in intervals (e.g., 0–20%, 20–40%, etc.) in which the first interval (0–20%) scored as 1, the second (20–40%) as 2, and so forth, meaning that possible overall scores could range between 5 and 25.

T levels in the saliva were measured by radioimmunoassay according to published protocols (Ellison, Lipson, & Meredith, 1989) in Harvard's Reproductive Ecology Laboratory.

After centrifugation, 1 ml of each sample was extracted twice in diethyl ether, and the extracted samples were run in assays using a specific antiserum (anti-T #250 supplied by G.D. Niswender, Colorado State University) and a four-position tritiated T competitor (Amersham). Assay sensitivity, the smallest amount of steroid distinguishable from zero with 95% confidence, averaged 16.2 pmol/l; T levels in the samples ranged from 37 to 1153 pmol/l. Interassay variability, estimated from high and low pools, was 10.0% for the high pool and 19.5% for the low pool, and intra-assay coefficients of variation averaged 8.1%. All samples from an individual were run in the same assay, and each assay included samples from unmarried men and married men with and without children. A mean a.m. and p.m. T value was calculated for each subject by averaging his two morning and two evening samples, respectively.

We used analysis of variance (ANOVA) for three-group comparisons. Student's t tests (paired and unpaired) and regression analyses were also employed where appropriate. All statistical tests were one-tailed because we predicted differences in specified directions.

3. Results

All T values fell within the normal range of values reported in other studies (Read, 1993), and T levels were lower in evening than in morning samples for all participants (paired t test; $t = 11.90$, $df = 56$, $P < .0001$), which is consistent with the circadian pattern of T secretion (Dabbs, 1990).

Since in our study (a.m. samples: $y = 756.8 - 7.7x$, $r^2 = .05$, $P = .10$; p.m. samples: $y = 536.3 - 8.2x$, $r^2 = .15$, $P = .003$) and in previous studies (e.g., Dabbs, 1990), male T levels decline with age, we had to control for age effects before we could investigate the

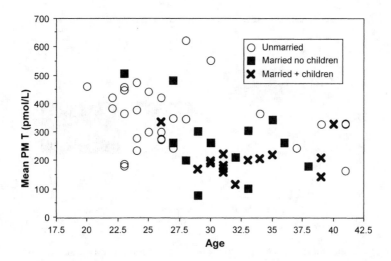

Fig. 1. Individual mean evening T levels plotted against age.

relationship between T and male mating and parenting status (see Fig. 1). We used the residuals of a linear regression of age on T to compare the status groups. These data supported our first prediction since after controlling for age, married men without children had significantly lower T levels than unmarried men (see Fig. 2 and Table 2). However, this difference was only true for evening samples (unpaired t test, a.m.: $t=1.18$, $df=41$, $P=.122$; p.m.: $t=1.41$, $df=41$, $P=.045$). Our second prediction was also partially supported by the data since T levels for fathers were significantly lower than T levels for unmarried men (unpaired t test, $t=3.45$, $df=42$, $P=.0005$) but were not significantly lower than levels for married men without children (unpaired t test, $t=1.30$, $df=27$, $P=.103$). Again, this difference was apparent only in evening samples (ANOVA, a.m.: $F=0.90$, $df=2$, $P=.413$; p.m.: $F=5.43$, $df=2$, $P=.001$; Fig. 2). Also, we found no significant difference among the groups in the mean change in T (mean a.m. − mean p.m.) over the course of the day after controlling for the effects of age (ANOVA: $F=0.693$, $df=2$, $P=.505$). To also control for other possible confounding factors that we derived from the T literature — BMI, exercise, stress — we entered age and relationship into a stepwise multiple regression model with these other variables. This analysis revealed that relationship status was the only significant predictor of evening T levels in our sample (relationship status: $\beta=-.521$, $P<.0005$; age: $\beta=-.228$, $P=.091$; BMI: $\beta=.021$, $P=.877$; exercise: $\beta=.089$, $P=.514$; stress: $\beta=.112$, $P=.412$).

Because the association between relationship status and T only held for evening samples, we tested Predictions 3 and 4 using only these values. Contrary to our predictions, we found that duration of marriage ($r_s=-.139$, $n=14$, $P=.317$) and our composite measure of "male parenting effort" ($r_s=.125$, $n=15$, $P=.328$) did not negatively correlate with evening T levels. Nor was age of youngest child positively correlated with evening T ($r_s=-.146$, $n=15$, $P=.302$). However, "spousal investment" scores and the amount of time participants spent with their spouses on their last day off work did negatively correlate with evening

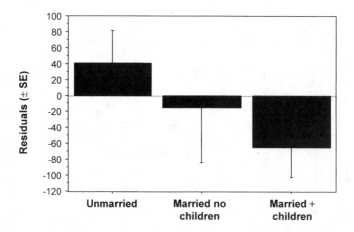

Fig. 2. Residuals (mean and S.E.) of evening T, controlling for age, for unmarried men and married men with and without children. T levels of married men with and without children are significantly lower than those of unmarried men.

Table 2
Mean (S.E.) a.m. and p.m. T levels (pmol/l) according to relationship status

	Unmarried men	Married without children	Fathers
n	29	14	15
Mean a.m. T (S.E.)	578.6 (40.2)	478.6 (55.5)	477.5 (33.1)
Mean p.m. T (S.E.)	350.2 (20.3)	267.7 (32.5)	203.5 (15.4)

T levels among married men without children (spousal investment: $r_s = -.515$, $n = 14$, $P = .030$; time spent with spouse: $r_s = -.645$, $n = 14$, $P = .006$).

4. Discussion

Controlling for age, we found that married men without children had lower evening T levels than unmarried men. Though fathers did not have significantly lower evening T levels than married men without children, fathers had markedly lower T levels compared with unmarried men. These results support the view that T mediates a tradeoff between mating and parenting effort in human males, as suggested by Wingfield et al.'s "challenge hypothesis." While unmarried men (higher T) invest only in mating effort, fathers (lower T) also invest in parenting effort, while presumably decreasing investment in mating effort.

The results also provide some support for our predictions relating T levels to variation in male spousal relationships and parenting. For two measures (a "spousal investment" score and reports of time participants spent with their spouses on their last day off work), our findings support the view that greater spousal investment corresponds with lower evening T levels. Our other predictions regarding the relationship between parenting effort and T were not supported by the data.

Our finding that evening, but not morning, male T levels are consistent with the predicted effects of relationship and parental status suggests that daily interactions, thoughts, and emotions may have modulating effects on male T. In keeping with this view, so-called "winner/loser" effects (in which T levels rise in competitors prior to a match, and remain higher in winners afterwards) show that short-term events can affect T levels (Mazur & Booth, 1998). Thus, we expected fathers to experience greater decreases in T across the day than unmarried men (controlling for age). Fathers did exhibit greater decreases across the day, but this difference was not significant (*t* test, unequal variance, $df = 40$, $P = .134$). The moderate sample size, and resulting low statistical power, might underlie this result. Certainly, this interpretation is in agreement with previous studies that have shown that hormonal signatures of social interactions are most evident in evening, rather than morning samples. For example, Muller and Wrangham (2001) found significant correlations between male chimpanzee urinary T and dominance rank in p.m., but not a.m. samples. Similarly, in their investigation of !Kung men, Worthman and Konner (1987) observed significant differences in T levels in p.m., but not a.m., serum samples when they compared levels on days when men hunted with levels on days when they did not hunt. Finally, the Berg and Wynne-Edwards (2001) study of expectant fathers observed significantly lower T levels compared with controls in p.m. but not a.m. samples.

Our work does not examine whether changes in T represent a cause or effect of behavior. We nonetheless propose a reciprocal model of T and mating and parenting behavior. Since it appears that T levels play a facilitatory role in competitive interactions among males (see Mazur & Booth, 1998), relationship stimuli (interacting with or thinking about a mate; interacting with or thinking about one's small child) that down-regulate male T levels during waking hours may alter the likelihood of individuals engaging in certain behaviors. In Wingfield et al.'s (1990) model, these lowered T levels translate into reduced mating effort. Alternatively, they may have the more direct benefit of facilitating direct paternal care (as suggested by the results in Storey et al., 2000). Engaging in mating and parenting behaviors might themselves then alter T levels, continuing this feedback process.

Much remains for future research in this area. Manipulations of physiological T levels in human males could examine the effects of T on attention to relevant social stimuli (e.g., an infant cry or threatening face: see Pope, Kouri, & Hudson, 2000). Cross-cultural study could examine variation in male T levels within societies in which males engage in different amounts of mating and parenting effort than our U.S. setting. An important implication of this research is the suggestion that variation in T may constitute part of the neuroendocrine basis of human paternal care.

Acknowledgments

This study was conducted in conjunction with a behavioral endocrinology research seminar at Harvard University. Permission to conduct this study was obtained from the Harvard University FAS Committee on the Use of Human Subjects. For helpful discussion, we would like to thank the participants in the behavioral endocrinology class and the anthropology department lunch seminar. We also thank Ben Campbell, Martin Daly, Melissa Emery, Martin Muller, Margo Wilson, Mike Wilson, and two anonymous reviewers for their valuable comments on drafts of this manuscript. Mary O'Rourke provided assistance in the lab and Steve Wang offered helpful statistical advice. Most of all, we would like to thank all the men who participated in the study.

References

Ball, G. F. (1991). Endocrine mechanisms and the evolution of avian parental care. *Acta XX Congressus Internationalis Ornithologici*, 984–992.

Berg, S. J., & Wynne-Edwards, K. E. (2001). Changes in testosterone, cortisol, estradiol levels in men becoming fathers. *Mayo Clinic Proceedings*, 76, 582–592.

Booth, A., & Dabbs Jr., J. M. (1993). Testosterone and men's marriages. *Social Forces*, 72, 463–477.

Campbell, B. C., & Leslie, P. W. (1995). Reproductive ecology of human males. *Yearbook of Physical Anthropology*, 38, 1–26.

Chisholm, J. S. (1999). *Death, hope and sex*. Cambridge: Cambridge University Press.

Cohen, S., Tamarck, T., & Mermelstein, R. (1983). A global measure of perceived stress. *Journal of Health and Social Behavior*, 24, 385–396.

Creel, S., Creel, N. M., Mills, M. G. L., & Monfort, S. L. (1997). Rank and reproduction in cooperatively breeding African wild dogs: behavioral and endocrine correlates. *Behavioral Ecology, 8*, 298–306.

Dabbs Jr., J. M. (1990). Salivary testosterone measurements: reliability across hours, days, weeks. *Physiology and Behavior, 48*, 83–86.

Daly, M., & Wilson, M. (1988). *Homicide*. New York: Aldine de Gruyter.

Draper, P., & Harpending, H. (1982). Father absence and reproductive strategy: an evolutionary perspective. *Journal of Anthropological Research, 38*, 255–273.

Ellison, P. T., Lipson, S. F., & Meredith, M. D. (1989). Salivary testosterone levels in males from the Ituri Forest of Zaire. *American Journal of Human Biology, 1*, 21–24.

Flinn, M., & Low, B. (1986). Resource distribution, social competition, mating patterns in human societies. In: D. Rubenstein, & R. W. Wrangham (Eds.), *Ecological aspects of social evolution* (pp. 217–243). Princeton: Princeton University Press.

Hewlett, B. S. (1992). *Father–child relations*. New York: Aldine de Gruyter.

Ketterson, E. D., & Nolan Jr., V. (1999). Adaptation, exaptation, constraint: a hormonal perspective. *American Naturalist, 154S*, S4–S25.

Lancaster, J. B., & Kaplan, H. (1992). Human mating and family formation strategies: the effects of variability among males in quality and the allocation of mating effort and parental investment. In: T. Nishida, W. C. McGrew, P. Marler, M. Pickford, & F. B. deWaal (Eds.), *Topics in primatology*, (vol. 1, pp. 21–33). Tokyo: University of Tokyo Press.

Lipson, S. F., & Ellison, P. T. (1989). Development of protocols for the application of salivary steroid analyses to field conditions. *American Journal of Human Biology, 1*, 249–255.

Lund, M. (1985). The development of investment and commitment scales for predicting continuity of personal relationships. *Journal of Social and Personal Relationships, 2*, 3–23.

Marlowe, F. (2000). Paternal investment and the human mating system. *Behavioural Processes, 51*, 45–61.

Mazur, A., & Booth, A. (1998). Testosterone and dominance in men. *Behavioral and Brain Sciences, 21*, 353–363.

Mazur, A., & Michalek, J. (1998). Marriage, divorce, male testosterone. *Social Forces, 77*, 315–330.

Muller, M. N., & Wrangham, R. W. (2001). The reproductive ecology of male hominoids. In: P. T. Ellison (Ed.), *Reproductive ecology and human evolution* (pp. 397–427). New York: Aldine de Gruyter.

Pope, H. G., Kouri, E., & Hudson, J. (2000). Effects of supraphysiological doses of testosterone on mood and aggression in normal men. *Archives of General Psychiatry, 57*, 133–140.

Read, G. F. (1993). Status report on measurement of salivary estrogens and androgens. *Annals of the New York Academy of Sciences, 694*, 146–160.

Storey, A. E., Walsh, C. J., Quinton, R. L., & Wynne-Edwards, K. E. (2000). Hormonal correlates of paternal responsiveness in new and expectant fathers. *Evolution and Human Behavior, 21*, 79–95.

Vermeulen, A., Goemaere, S., & Kaufman, J. M. (1999). Testosterone, body composition and aging. *Journal of Endocrinological Investigation, 22*, 110–116.

Wingfield, J. C., Hegner, R. E., Dufty Jr., A. M., & Ball, G. F. (1990). The "challenge hypothesis": theoretical implications for patterns of testosterone secretion, mating systems, breeding strategies. *American Naturalist, 136*, 829–846.

Worthman, C. M., & Konner, M. J. (1987). Testosterone levels change with subsistence hunting effort in !Kung San men. *Psychoneuroendocrinology, 12*, 449–458.

Wynne-Edwards, K. E. (2001). Hormonal changes in mammalian fathers. *Hormones and Behavior, 40*, 139–145.

Ziegler, T. E. (2000). Hormones associated with non-maternal infant studies: a review of mammalian and avian studies. *Folia Primatologia, 71*, 6–21.

ELSEVIER

Evolution and Human Behavior 23 (2002) 203–231

Evolution
and Human
Behavior

Punitive sentiment as an anti-free rider psychological device

Michael E. Price[a,*], Leda Cosmides[b], John Tooby[a]

[a]*Department of Anthropology, Center for Evolutionary Psychology, University of California, Santa Barbara, CA 93106, USA*
[b]*Department of Psychology, University of California, Santa Barbara, CA 93106, USA*

Received 3 August 2000; received in revised form 24 August 2001; accepted 13 September 2001

Abstract

Those who contribute to a public good sometimes experience punitive sentiments toward others. But is the system that produces these sentiments an adaptation and, if so, which collective action problem was it designed to solve? Prior results from experimental economics show that acts of free riding are sometimes punished, that punishment deters free riding, and that the risk or actuality of punishment recruits higher levels of cooperation in a joint effort. This suggests that one function of punitive sentiments could be to recruit labor for collective actions. However, adaptations designed to cause participation in collective actions could not have evolved unless there were some mechanism that protected those who participated from having lower fitness than nonparticipating free riders. Therefore, a second possible function of punishment could be to eliminate or reverse fitness differentials that favor free rider designs over participant designs. To map the computational structure of this motivational adaptation (and hence identify its specific function) requires data that relate an individual's circumstances to his or her desire to punish. Herein, we report such data. The results indicate that the computational system that regulates one's level of punitive sentiment in collective action contexts is functionally specialized for removing the fitness advantage enjoyed by free riders rather than for labor recruitment or other functions. Results also support the hypothesis that a separate pro-reward motivational system exists that appears designed to handle the problem of labor recruitment. Rational choice counterexplanations for punitive sentiments were considered but eliminated on the basis of the evidence. © 2002 Elsevier Science Inc. All rights reserved.

Keywords: Collective action; Altruism; Punishment; Morality; Cooperation; Public goods; Rational choice

* Corresponding author.
E-mail addresses: mep2@umail.ucsb.edu (M.E. Price), cosmides@psych.ucsb.edu (L. Cosmides), tooby@anth.ucsb.edu (J. Tooby).

1090-5138/02/$ – see front matter © 2002 Elsevier Science Inc. All rights reserved.
PII: S1090-5138(01)00093-9

1. Introduction

Individual participation in collective action is one of the most intensively discussed issues in the behavioral sciences for a simple reason. It is, at present, a phenomenon in search of an explanation. On the one hand, it is clear that individual humans routinely and willingly participate in projects that require collective action: Sets of individuals will cooperate to achieve a common goal even when the rewards to individuals are not intrinsically linked to individual effort. Cooperation to provide a public good happens not just in agricultural and industrial societies but in hunter-gatherer and hunter-horticulturist ones as well. Plausible examples include cooperative hunting and food sharing (Gurven, Hill, Kaplan, Hurtado, & Lyles, 2000; Hawkes, 1993; Kelly, 1995; Lee & DeVore, 1968; Smith, 1985), offensive raids and collective defense (reviews in Keeley, 1996; Wrangham & Peterson, 1996), cooperative shelter building (Chagnon, 1997; Harner, 1984), and field clearings (Holmberg, 1969; Smole, 1976). On the other hand, game theoretical analyses in economics and biology have shown that the incentives individuals face in many collective action problems are insufficient to promote voluntary contributions to public goods and instead favor free riding and defection as the equilibrium outcome (Hardin, 1968; Olson, 1965; for reviews of studies related to collective action problems, see Ledyard, 1995; Ostrom, 1998). These impediments to collective action hold, whether the currency is monetary payoffs to a rational actor or fitness payoffs to alternative heritable neurocognitive design features. How, then, could selection have favored the spread of psychological design features that cause participation in collective action? That is, how should the fact that people often willingly sacrifice for their coalition, country, political party, or residential group be explained? Is this behavior an incidental byproduct of psychological mechanisms designed for some other purpose, or is it the signature of an adaptation that evolved specifically for collective action under ancestral conditions? (For discussion, see Alexander, 1987; Patton, 1996; Stern, 1995; Tooby & Cosmides, 1988; Wright, 1994.)

Recent models of the evolution of collective action have focused on the role of punishment (Boyd & Richerson, 1992; Gintis, 2000; Henrich & Boyd, 2001). These models show that willingness to contribute to a public good can be evolutionarily stable as long as free riders are punished, along with those who refuse to punish free riders. Moreover, research in experimental economics using public goods games has shown that higher levels of cooperation result when the probability that free riding will be punished is large enough (Fehr & Gächter, 2000a; Kurzban, McCabe, Smith, & Wilson, 2001). More puzzling from a game theory and selectionist standpoint, the results of these studies clearly show that individuals are willing to incur personal costs in order to punish free riders (Dawes, Orbell, & Van de Kragt, 1986; Fehr & Gächter, 2000a; Ostrom, Walker, & Gardner, 1992; Sato, 1987; Yamagishi, 1992). They do this even when it appears that they are unlikely to have future interactions with the individual they punished and, therefore, are unlikely to recoup their losses in the form of increased cooperation from that person in the future (for review, see Gintis, 2000).

Unfortunately, these results do not make the evolution of adaptations for collective action any less mysterious. Because punishing a free rider would generally have entailed some nontrivial cost, each potential punisher has an incentive to defect — that is, to avoid this cost by not punishing acts of free riding. Thus, the provision of punishment is itself a public good: Each individual has an incentive to free ride on the punishment activities of others (Henrich & Boyd, 2001; Sober & Wilson, 1998; Yamagishi, 1986). Hence, second-order free riders should be fitter (or better off) than punishers. Without a way of solving this second-order free rider problem, cooperation should unravel, with nonparticipation and nonpunishment the equilibrium outcome. Even worse, this problem reappears at each new level, revealing an infinite regress problem: Punishment needs to be visited on free riders on the original public good, and on those who do not punish free riders, and on those who do not punish those who do not punish free riders, and so on. A number of models — some invoking group selection (Gintis, 2000), others not (Boyd & Richerson, 1992; Henrich & Boyd, 2001; Hirshleifer & Rasmusen, 1989; Tooby & Cosmides, 1988) — have been proposed to solve this problem. All have problems, and there is no consensus yet on which is most likely to be correct.

How adaptations for collective action could have evolved given the free rider problem is puzzling at present; 30 years ago, selectionists were wondering how sexual recombination could have evolved given the cost of meiosis. At the time, none of the existing models were fully adequate (Williams, 1975). Nevertheless, as Williams pointed out, one could still draw sound conclusions about the functions of many subcomponents of sexual reproduction, despite the fact that other aspects remained mysterious (including its ultimate function):

> The machinery of sexual reproduction in higher animals and plants is unmistakably an evolved adaptation. It is complex, remarkably uniform, and clearly directed at the goal of producing, with the genes of two parental individuals, offspring of diverse genotypes. How the production of diverse rather than uniform offspring contributes to the ultimate goal of reproductive survival may not be immediately obvious, but the precision of the machinery can only be explained on the basis of selection for efficiency in the production of offspring with the parental genes but not the parental genotypes. (Williams, 1966, p. 125)

The point is this: When selectionist theories have hit an impasse, one can often make headway by applying adaptationist tools (Williams, 1966, 1975). By exploring what sets of outcomes each subcomponent of an adaptive system seems narrowly designed to produce, one may be able to deduce their functions, i.e., the selection pressures that built the machinery.

We think that punitive and pro-reward motivational circuitry can be approached in this fashion. Unlike meiosis and gametogenesis, however, the motivational responses in humans to situations of collective action are not yet mapped with enough resolution to determine whether they are adaptations. But by mapping their internal interrelationships — what outcomes (motivations, decisions, and behaviors) they produce and what variables regulate those outcomes — we think progress can be made in discovering their design and, eventually, their adaptive function (if any).

Therefore, we wish to raise the following questions: Is there evolved neurocognitive circuitry that causes people to punish free riders in collective action contexts? More importantly, does our motivational system show sufficient evidence of special design for this outcome that we should conclude it is a solution to the problem of punishing free riders, rather than a byproduct or maladaptive misfiring of a mechanism designed for solving some other kind of problem? If the answers to these questions are yes, then this raises a third, less explored question: What exactly was the selective advantage of punishment in ancestral collective action contexts — that is, what was the functional consequence of punishing?

The existing evidence, while suggestive, is not sufficient to answer these questions. Research in experimental economics shows that (1) people are willing to incur unreimbursed costs to punish others (a puzzle), (2) overall levels of cooperation are higher when opportunities to punish free riders exist (an unsurprising outcome that would be produced simply by a general ability to anticipate and respond to incentives, assuming punishment is anticipated), and (3) *average* levels of punishment are greater the more a free rider's contribution falls below the average contribution of the other group members (e.g., Fehr & Gächter, 2000a, 2000b). However, this research does not include analyses of individual choices to cooperate and punish, to see if and how the two are connected. Specifically, the data presented so far do not tell us whether a connection exists — and if so, how large it is — between an *individual's* willingness to contribute to the provision of a (first-order) public good and that individual's willingness to punish free riders. Nor do these data tell us whether one's willingness to punish is better predicted by one's willingness to contribute to a public good or by some other, possibly correlated variable, such as the perception that one will personally benefit from a collective action. The study reported herein was designed to address these issues.

1.1. Punitive sentiment as an anti-free rider psychological device

By a punitive sentiment, we mean the designed expression of evolved, reliably developing circuitry in the motivational system: specifically, a desire that the target of the sentiment be harmed. (Additional features could include the desires that (1) the target be aware of being harmed, (2) the target know why, and (3) others be aware of the reason for the punishment.) Consistent with the proposals of many researchers, we hypothesize that there is a motivational adaptation that evolved specifically to cause punitive sentiments toward free riders, with free riders being defined (by the computational adaptation) as individuals who (1) benefit from a collective action, (2) could have contributed to the success of the joint effort without incurring a cost disproportionately greater than their share of the expected benefit, and (3) did not expend adequate effort toward the collective action. The more punitive sentiment this circuitry generates, the more the experiencer is induced to take punitive action despite the existence of collateral costs or motivations that would otherwise deter such action.

An adaptation causing punitive sentiments toward nonparticipants in a collective action could have increased the probability that free riders were actually punished in three distinct but nonexclusive ways. First, it could motivate the experiencer to inflict punishment personally, independent of the actions of others and despite some personal cost. In this case, the sentiment would also act as a commitment mechanism (Frank, 1988; Hirshleifer, 1987). Indeed, there is some evidence that those who incur costs to punish in public goods games were angered by acts of free riding (Andreoni, 1995). Second, a punitive sentiment could have induced its experiencer to participate in or proportionately subsidize punishment efforts provided they are joint, since these levy a smaller personal cost than unilateral acts of punishment. By definition, joint punishments reduce or eliminate the possibility of second-order free riding. Third, it could have induced the experiencer to advocate punishment of free riders without subsidizing it (although the functional dynamics of advocacy compared to other kinds of action depend on other assumptions about the social environment). Not all coalition members would have had to participate equally in every act of punishment to deter free riding. By supporting a punishment norm, advocacy could help advertise the high costs of free riding (thereby deterring it) and perhaps induce others to punish by making it clear that their efforts will not be opposed (e.g., Henrich & Boyd, 2001).

What features of special design should we expect in a system designed for motivating the punishment of nonparticipants? The answer differs depending on exactly which adaptive problem this punitive sentiment evolved to solve.

1.2. Recruiting participants or eliminating adverse fitness differentials?

An adaptation that causes punitive sentiments toward nonparticipants in a collective action could have two separate, though compatible, functions:

1. It could be designed to increase the probability that a public good will be successfully provided. Such an adaptation would be designed to accomplish this by encouraging otherwise reluctant parties to participate more fully in a collective action (Alexander, 1987; Cronk, 1994; Irons, 1991; Sato, 1987; Tooby & Cosmides, 1988). The threat of punishment could increase participation from three different labor pools: (a) free riders, (b) nonparticipants who are not free riders,[1] and (c) non-free riding participants who, through working even harder, could increase the public good.

---

[1] Indeed, given the definition of free riding that we propose is built into our psychology, it should be clear that one can refrain from participating in a collective action without being a free rider for several distinct reasons. Nonparticipants who do not take or accrue the rewards of a collective action are not free riders; nor are those who, due to injury, pregnancy, or other reasons, are incapable of contributing. If only free riders are the targets of punishment, then these other categories of individual should be seen as exempt. Moreover, it is worthwhile to distinguish actors according to the degree they benefit from the collective action, their costs of participating, and whether they participated. Those whose benefits from a collective action would have exceeded their costs of participating and yet do not participate are free riders by any useful definition. In contrast, one could take two views about whether the following set of individuals is usefully categorized as free riders: those for whom the cost of participating in a collective action would have exceeded their benefit from that collective action, and so do not participate. If they participated, they would be the victims of exploitation, contributing to others' net benefits while incurring a net deficit themselves. If they failed to participate, they would be getting benefits out of the efforts of others without contributing to their production. An interesting question is, therefore, which of the two definitions is embodied in the decision-making psychology of collective action: Are they categorized as free riders or exempt nonparticipants? We suspect that under more egalitarian conditions, our psychology does not categorize them as free riders. To exempt these individuals from punishment — that is, to categorize them as non-free riders — is more evolutionarily stable. After all, the alternative — a collective action system that punished these individuals — would be pitting itself against adaptations that resist exploitation. We suspect, however, that when a sufficient number of individuals interested in the collective action are powerfully situated, they switch to the more exploitive definition of free rider, and include those whose costs of participating exceed the benefits of the action as suitable targets of punishment.

2. Punitive sentiments toward nonparticipants could be designed to eliminate the fitness advantage free riders accrue over participants in collective action by inducing participants to proportionately damage the fitness of free riders (Tooby & Cosmides, 1996). By definition, both free riders and participants in collective action enjoy its benefits, but the participants pay a cost that free riders do not and so suffer from a relative fitness disadvantage. Design features that motivate participation in collective action could not have been systematically favored or be evolutionarily stable unless the free riders' default fitness advantage had been somehow eliminated or reversed.

Eliminating the fitness advantage of free riding is a separate adaptive function from maximizing the profitability of a collective action venture through optimizing the number of participants recruited. Punitive sentiments in collective actions could have been designed to accomplish either, both, or neither of these adaptive functions. Because each function carries different predictions, it is possible to test among these alternatives. Of course, because of the way the world is structured, punishment sufficient to eliminate the fitness benefits of free riding may also have the collateral effect of encouraging participation — it may motivate the participation of individuals who would otherwise free ride. Nevertheless, the predictions remain sufficiently different that progress can be made differentiating these two functions.

In addition, it is commonplace for different components of adaptive machinery to solve different but interlocking adaptive problems — the eye, for example, has a lens for focusing light and rhodopsin for registering its presence. Similarly, the two functions of optimizing labor recruitment and eliminating adverse fitness differentials need not be handled by precisely the same behavior-regulatory circuit logic. Furthermore, the adaptive problem posed by the potential proliferation of nonpunishers (as second-order free riders) may not be solved by the same means and circuitry as the adaptive problem created by the potential proliferation of nonparticipants or undercontributors (as first-order free riders). This means that we can treat these three adaptive problems independently, and proceed to test competing hypotheses about the adaptive function of punitive sentiments toward first-order free riders without knowing how the adaptive problem of second-order free riding has been solved. Once the function of punishing first-order free riders is clarified, we can see if this throws light on competing theories of how the problem of second- and higher-order free riding on punishers might have been solved.

1.2.1. Recruiting participants

There are many evolutionarily recurrent contexts — war being the most obvious — in which success in providing a public good (e.g., defense) may be a function of either how many individuals participate or the degree to which participants expend effort (Tooby & Cosmides, 1988; Wrangham & Peterson, 1996). This means that the problem of recruiting sufficiently many participants (or sufficiently effortful participants) would have often occurred. Moreover, the experimental work by Fehr and Gächter (2000a) shows that the same individuals contribute at higher levels when the possibility of punishment exists than when it does not, showing that punishment is in fact effective at mobilizing higher rates and levels of participation. Whether this is punishment's selectively designed function or merely a beneficial byproduct remains to be determined.

Listing all of the design features expected of a system whose function was to optimize recruitment is beyond the scope of this article, but certain predictions are relevant to this study.

(a) If encouraging participation by otherwise reluctant individuals is one adaptive function of a system that causes punitive sentiments toward nonparticipants, then those who are most likely to benefit from the achievement of a group goal should differentially act to induce others to achieve this goal (e.g., Alexander, 1987, pp. 191–192; Cronk, 1994; Irons, 1991). More specifically, the adaptation should be designed such that the greater an individual's expected benefit from a successfully executed collective action, the more punitive sentiment that individual will experience.

(b) The predicted relationship between own expected benefit and sentiment for punishing others should remain significant, even when one controls for the individual's own willingness to participate. After all, encouraging self-sacrificial participation by others provides the largest net benefit, even for a free rider.

(c) If encouraging participation by others is this adaptation's *only* function, then after controlling for perceived benefit, any relationship between the individual's willingness to participate and punitive sentiment toward others should disappear.

(d) Sentiment for rewarding participants should track sentiment for punishing nonpartici- pants. There is nothing inherent in the problem of labor recruitment that privileges punishment over reward as an incentive — each might serve to motivate recruitment. If the function of punitive sentiment is purely for motivating recruitment, then sentiment for rewarding participants should be correlated with sentiment for punishing nonparticipants, since they both serve the same function.

Equally important (although not testable in this study) are three further predictions:

(e) If optimizing labor recruitment were the overriding selection pressure designing punitive sentiments toward nonparticipants, then this system should be sensitive only to the labor needs of the collective action, not to the existence of free riders per se. The target of punitive sentiments ought to be those whose punishment-inducible participation would most help the collective action, not those nonparticipants who differentially benefit by the collective action. Once the manpower needs of the collective action are satisfied, a system with this function should be indifferent to the prospering of free riders, and their continued presence should not provoke punitive sentiments.

(f) Equally, a system designed to optimize recruitment should be indifferent to whether a nonparticipant is a free rider (i.e., someone for whom the collective action is beneficial) or not. What matters is whether a potential recruit's participation would be beneficial to the collective action, not whether the collective action helps or harms the recruit. This is the reverse of what would be expected if the function were to eliminate the fitness advantages of free riders. In that case, a nonparticipant who does not benefit by a collective action is not a free rider, regardless of how much his or her participation would help in provisioning the collective good. If punitive sentiments were designed exclusively to punish free riders, then nonparticipants who do not benefit from the collective action but who could have helped it succeed ought not to stimulate punitive sentiments.

(g) Finally, because the function of a participation-managing system is to induce others to contribute in a way that maximally benefits the incentive-manipulator, individuals who contribute anything less than the optimal amount might be suitable targets for punishment. Indeed, if participation management is the function, those who benefit the most from a collective action should feel punitive even toward individuals who *do* contribute at an average level, if this would encourage them to contribute even more. (Evidence from other studies relevant to this prediction will be discussed in Section 4.)

1.2.2. Eliminating adverse fitness differentials

In evolving populations, heritable designs are selected for to the extent they exhibit a fitness advantage relative to their competitors. Because characteristics that create a relative fitness advantage are not always the same as those which maximize absolute returns, adaptationist predictions sometimes diverge from the predictions of rational choice theory. In the case of collective action, collective producers realize benefits from productive action that nonlocal nonproducers do not, and so enjoy higher fitness compared to them. Unfortunately, local designs that free ride enjoy even higher relative fitness and so outcompete simple producers. Reversing this relative fitness advantage is mandatory if designs that reap the benefits of producing through collective action are to prevail. Adaptations in producers might be expected to evolve, even if they lower absolute returns, provided they lower the returns to free riders even more, thereby creating a relative fitness advantage for producers over free riders.

Eliminating or reversing this adverse fitness differential is a specific, logically distinct adaptive problem that could have selected for neurocognitive circuitry narrowly specialized solely for this task. Moreover, the outputs of such circuitry might appear nonrational (i.e., individually costly) or even spiteful because their function is to reverse relative fitness orderings rather than to maximize returns (Tooby & Cosmides, 1996). Hence, an alternative hypothesis for the function of punitive sentiments is to motivate actions that remove or reverse the fitness differential that would accrue to free riders relative to producers in the absence of punishment.

The hypothesis that punitive sentiments toward nonparticipants were designed to eliminate the fitness advantage of free riders predicts the following:

(a) The individual's own participation is the specific factor that should trigger punitive sentiments toward free riders. This is because only those individuals who contribute to a collective action are at risk of incurring lower fitness relative to free riders.

(b) The more an individual contributes, the greater the adverse fitness differential s/he potentially suffers relative to free riders. A sentiment designed to redress adverse fitness differentials and prevent outcompetition by free riders should therefore key the *degree* of punitive sentiment toward free riders to the individual's own willingness to participate in a collective action. The more willing the individual is to participate, the more that individual should wish to see free riders punished.

(c) This relationship between participation and punitive sentiment should be specific and selective: Punitive sentiment should track willingness to participate strongly even when one controls for other variables. For example, individuals may differ in the extent to which they will benefit if a collective action succeeds. Accordingly, the perception that one will benefit from a successful collective action should be positively correlated with one's willingness to participate. Even when benefits are equal, however, the costs of participation will inevitably vary from individual to individual, making the correlation between perception of benefit and willingness to participate imperfect at best. However, it is participation per se and not degree of benefit that makes the design vulnerable to free riding. Therefore, it is participation rather than the benefit derived that should — on this theory — predict punitive sentiment. If this is true, then punitiveness should track willingness to participate strongly even after any effects of perception of benefit are statistically removed.

(d) If preventing adverse fitness differentials were the adaptation's *only* function, then after controlling for willingness to participate, any relationship between perceived benefit and punitive sentiment should disappear.

(e) Willingness to participate should predict punishment, but not reward. Punishment is better suited to eliminating adverse fitness differentials than reward is (even though reward remains an effective way of solving problems of labor recruitment). When reward induces a free riding underproducer to join a collective action, this preserves the underproducer's relative fitness advantage compared to the producer design that is doing the rewarding. If redressing adverse fitness differentials created by free riding is an adaptive problem the human mind was designed to solve, then this function should be differentially linked to punishment over reward.

(f) This means that reward sentiments *should not* track punitive sentiments, especially among those most willing to participate. In contrast, if labor recruitment were an important adaptive function of punitive sentiments toward nonparticipants, then reward and punishment sentiments should be correlated, especially among those with the greatest interest in seeing the common goal achieved.

Note that distinguishing between these two functions — participant recruitment and eliminating adverse fitness differentials — would be difficult on the basis of behavioral data alone (especially aggregate data). Behavioral data tell *whether* an individual contributed, free rode, and/or punished, but not why. In contrast, survey data can assess the perceptions and attitudes necessary to test between these two hypotheses.

1.2.3. Both functions

If punitive sentiment toward nonparticipants evolved in the service of both functions — encouraging otherwise reluctant participants and preventing adverse fitness differentials — then it should be correlated with both predictor variables: perceived benefit to the individual of the collective action and that individual's willingness to participate. Moreover, both correlations should stand, even when one controls for any correlation between these two predictor variables.

1.2.4. Byproduct?

It is difficult to make a prediction without knowing which adaptation punitive sentiments toward free riders are supposed to be a byproduct of. In the absence of a specific proposal, the zero-level prediction is a random relationship between functional variables (Tooby & Cosmides, 1989). If punitive sentiment does not track the functional variables described above, then it might track demographic ones instead, such as ethnicity or birth order (as has been suggested by Carroll, Perkowitz, Lurigio, & Weaver, 1987; Davis, Severy, Kraus, &

Whitaker, 1993; Sulloway, 1996). Or, there might be a general appetite to punish wrong-doing, independent of type. For example, one might find that willingness to participate predicts punishment of free riders no more than punishment of other forms of wrongdoing. This would suggest that willingness to participate activates punitive sentiments *in general* rather than ones specifically designed to remove the fitness advantage of free riding.

In contrast, the adaptationist hypotheses above predict no *independent* relationship between demographic variables and punitive sentiment (i.e., unmediated by willingness to participate or perceived benefit). They also predict no particular relationship between punitiveness toward free riders and punitiveness toward criminals or other wrongdoers.

The most widely believed byproduct hypothesis is that behavior and sentiments are generated in accordance with the economic concept of rationality — that is, people have an adaptation that somehow calculates which course of action will maximize their individual payoffs, and choose their behavior and sentiments on this basis. Of course, punishment in collective action contexts is almost always irrational in this sense, because individuals incur costs to punish under circumstances where it is clear to a rational actor that no compensation for these costs could ensue (Fehr & Gächter, 2000a). For this reason, punitive sentiments cannot be explained as the expression of, or as a byproduct of, "rationality," "intelligence," or "rational choice." Nevertheless, we will dissect compo-nents of the rational choice hypothesis in Section 4 as well as a more relaxed form of this hypothesis: that people naturally favor the adoption of rules, norms, and incentives that benefit them (whether or not they always behave in a rationally cost-effective manner in support of them).

1.3. Sentiments for rewarding participation in collective action

The goal of encouraging others to participate in a collective action could be achieved either through the carrot or the stick. Above, we focused on how punitive sentiments might help encourage the reluctant to participate. However, researchers have long noted that cooperators "are sometimes motivated by a desire to win prestige, respect, friendship, and other social and psychological objectives" (Olson, 1965, p. 60). This suggests that one way to encourage participation in a collective action is to reward participants in a way that exceeds what they would get from the mere provision of the public good (Andreoni, 1990; Hawkes, 1993; Sober & Wilson, 1998). Many anthropologists have argued that in environ-ments most similar to those in which humans evolved, reward (especially, increased social status) apparently does motivate individuals to provide public goods such as food (Hawkes, 1993; Lemonnier, 1996; Sugiyama, 1996) and military service (Chagnon, 1988; Patton, 1996, 2000; Watson, 1971).

Hence, it seems likely that there are motivational adaptations for providing rewards to those who contribute to collective actions. An obvious design feature is that these pro-reward sentiments should be keyed to the degree to which the sentiment holder is likely to benefit from a collective action. In fact, if recruiting more participation were a selection pressure designing pro-reward sentiments, then one might expect own interest in the goal to predict pro-reward sentiments, even after controlling for one's willingness to participate. For example, due to injury, ineligibility, family obligations, or other circumstances, an individual may be unable to participate directly in a collective action that would be self-beneficial (Chagnon, 1997). Yet, that individual may be able to increase the endeavor's chances of success by providing rewards to those who can participate, but who otherwise might not.

Our goal herein is to expose the design of the motivational adaptations deployed in collective action. Each adaptive function discussed above implies a different design: Each makes different predictions about the conditions that trigger punitive (and pro-reward) sentiments in collective action. To test these predictions, a survey was conducted as described below.

2. Method

Data were collected by pencil-and-paper survey. Subjects were 18–25-year-old undergraduate US citizens at the University of California, Santa Barbara ($N = 287$), 53% ($n = 152$) of whom were female and 47% ($n = 135$) male. Fifty eight percent took the survey voluntarily in an anthropology class, and 42% were paid US$4 to take it after they approached a campus booth that was set up for the purpose of recruiting subjects. Subjects were asked to report their sex, ethnicity, age, birth order, and annual parental income.

Subjects read two different scenarios describing warfare between the USA and foreign countries (both scenarios are presented fully in the Appendix). The first scenario described the USA mobilizing *defensively* in reaction to a Russian invasion of Alaska. The second scenario described the USA mobilizing *offensively* in order to attack several Middle Eastern countries that had radically increased the price of oil. (Two scenarios rather than one were included so that we could confirm that a significant result in one scenario was not a fluke; both a defensive and offensive scenario were used so that we could detect any signs of "separate psychologies of offense and defense" hypothesized by Tooby and Cosmides, 1988, p. 9.) In both scenarios, subjects were told that the USA was going to have to start drafting citizens in order to have a chance of winning the war.

Following each scenario, subjects were presented with four statements and asked to respond on a 1–7 Likert-like scale from "disagree strongly" to "agree strongly." The first two items were the predictor variables. "If the USA won this war, it would be very good for me as an individual" measured how much subjects perceived that they would benefit from collective success, and will be referred to as SELF-INTEREST IN GROUP GOAL. "If I got drafted for this war, I would probably agree to serve" measured how willing subjects would be to participate in the collective action, and will be referred to as WILLINGNESS TO PARTICIPATE. Next came the two dependent variables. "If a US citizen resisted this draft, I'd think they should be punished" measured punitive sentiment toward nonparticipants, and will be referred to as PUNISH NONPARTICIPANTS. "If a drafted US citizen agreed to serve in this war, I'd think they should be rewarded" measured pro-reward sentiment toward participants, and will be referred to as REWARD PARTICIPANTS. The questionnaire also included a short battery of questions that assess attitudes toward punishment in general (focusing on crime; Carroll et al., 1987), which will be referred to as GENERAL

PUNITIVENESS; whether this battery appeared at the beginning or end was counterbalanced across subjects.

A total of 122 subjects (43%) received surveys in which the order of the dependent variables was reversed, i.e., surveys in which WILLINGNESS TO PARTICIPATE was followed first by REWARD PARTICIPANTS and then by PUNISH NONPARTICIPANTS instead of vice versa. Item order was manipulated in this way to ensure that correlations between WILLINGNESS TO PARTICIPATE and the dependent variables were unaffected by the proximity of the dependent variables to WILLINGNESS TO PARTICIPATE.

3. Results

Two types of correlations are shown in Table 1: simple correlations between each predictor and each dependent variable, and partial correlations between each predictor and each dependent variable when controlling for the effects of the other predictor variable. Also shown are each variable's mean and standard deviation.

3.1. Is there a relationship between a person's willingness to participate in a collective action and that individual's belief that s/he would personally benefit from that action?

Yes. There was a significant and positive correlation between WILLINGNESS TO PARTICIPATE and SELF-INTEREST IN GROUP GOAL in both scenarios [$r_{defensive} = .379$, $r_{offensive} = .276$, P's $< .001$ (all reported P values are two-tailed)].

Table 1
Simple and partial correlations in each scenario

	Punish nonparticipants ($M=2.77$, S.D.$=1.83$)		Reward participants ($M=5.22$, S.D.$=1.71$)	
Defensive scenario	Simple r	Partial r	Simple r	Partial r
Self-interest in group goal ($M=4.16$, S.D.$=1.69$)	.296***	.092	.296***	.272***
Willingness to participate ($M=3.27$, S.D.$=2.06$)	.597***	.548***	.121*	.010
	Punish nonparticipants ($M=2.37$, S.D.$=1.73$)		Reward participants ($M=4.72$, S.D.$=1.88$)	
Offensive scenario	Simple r	Partial r	Simple r	Partial r
Self-interest in group goal ($M=4.23$, S.D.$=1.88$)	.246***	.092	.369***	.351***
Willingness to participate ($M=2.56$, S.D.$=1.86$)	.648***	.623***	.125*	.025

* $P<.05$.
*** $P<.001$.

3.2. Which predicts punitive sentiment better, willingness to participate in a collective action or self-interest in group goal?

WILLINGNESS TO PARTICIPATE and SELF-INTEREST IN GROUP GOAL were both correlated with PUNISH NONPARTICIPANTS. However, the simple correlation for WILL-INGNESS TO PARTICIPATE was much higher than that for SELF-INTEREST IN GROUP GOAL (a result that holds for both the offensive and defensive scenarios).

Given that WILLINGNESS TO PARTICIPATE and SELF-INTEREST IN GROUP GOAL were correlated with each other leads to the more interesting question: How much of the variance in punitive sentiment is predicted by each variable, controlling for the other? When one controls for WILLINGNESS TO PARTICIPATE, the correlation between SELF-INTER-EST IN GROUP GOAL and PUNISH NONPARTICIPANTS plummeted to .092 in both scenarios (simple r's were .246 and .296, respectively). In contrast, when one controls for SELF-INTEREST IN GROUP GOAL, the correlation between WILLINGNESS TO PAR-TICIPATE and PUNISH NONPARTICIPANTS remained high (partial r's: $r_{defensive} = .548$, $r_{offensive} = .623$, P's $< .001$). Indeed, the partial r's for WILLINGNESS TO PARTICIPATE were almost as high as the simple r's. (N.B. The relationship between willingness to participate and punitive sentiment held for each sex separately; see Section 3.8.)

In short, a large and significant amount of the variance in subjects' punitive sentiment was predicted by their willingness to participate in a collective action, whereas very little of this variance was predicted by their perceived self-interest in the group goal being achieved.

3.3. Does willingness to participate in a collective action predict a desire to punish wrongdoing in general, or does it specifically activate the desire to punish free riders in the collective action?

There was a small but significant positive correlation between WILLINGNESS TO PARTICIPATE and GENERAL PUNITIVENESS ($r_{defensive} = .148$, $r_{offensive} = .138$, P's $< .05$). This simple correlation does not answer the question, however, because GENERAL PUNITIVENESS and PUNISH NONPARTICIPANTS were also weakly correlated ($r_{defensive} = .175$, $r_{offensive} = .179$, P's $< .05$). Thus, the correlation between WILLINGNESS TO PARTICIPATE and GENERAL PUNITIVENESS could reflect nothing more than the robust correlation reported above between WILLINGNESS TO PARTICIPATE and PUNISH NONPARTICIPANTS.

That appears to be the case. When one statistically controls for the effects of PUNISH NONPARTICIPANTS, the correlation between WILLINGNESS TO PARTICIP-ATE and GENERAL PUNITIVENESS disappears (partial r's: $r_{defensive} = .065$, $r_{offensive} = .035$, n.s.). Moreover, when one statistically controls for the effects of WILL-INGNESS TO PARTICIPATE, the relationship between PUNISH NONPARTICIPANTS and GENERAL PUNITIVENESS also dwindled to nonsignificance (partial r's: $r_{defensive} = .110$, $r_{offensive} = .124$, n.s.).

In sum, WILLINGNESS TO PARTICIPATE did not predict GENERAL PUNITIVENESS once the effects of PUNISH NONPARTICIPANTS were removed. Instead, willingness to participate was specifically and selectively associated with a desire to punish nonparticipants in the collective action in which one was participating.

3.4. Which is better predicted by a person's willingness to participate in a collective action: punitive sentiment or a wish to reward?

Consistent with the notion that reward is unsuitable for removing the fitness advantage of free riders, the partial correlation between WILLINGNESS TO PARTICIPATE and REWARD PARTICIPANTS was low and not significant (partial r's: $r_{defensive} = .010$, $r_{offensive} = .025$). This is in marked contrast to the partial correlation between WILLINGNESS TO PARTICIPATE and PUNISH NONPARTICIPANTS, which was positive, large, and significant (partial r's: $r_{defensive} = .548$, $r_{offensive} = .623$). And indeed, WILLINGNESS TO PARTICIPATE correlated significantly more positively (P's of $\Delta F < .001$) with PUNISH NONPARTICIPANTS ($r_{defensive} = .597$, $r_{offensive} = .648$, P's $< .001$) than with REWARD PARTICIPANTS ($r_{defensive} = .121$, $r_{offensive} = .125$, P's $< .05$).

There were no order effects. In both scenarios, correlations between WILLINGNESS TO PARTICIPATE and PUNISH NONPARTICIPANTS and WILLINGNESS TO PARTICIPATE and REWARD PARTICIPANTS were unaffected by whether PUNISH NONPARTICIPANTS came before or after REWARD PARTICIPANTS in the survey (P's of ΔF due to item order $> .704$).

3.5. Does labor recruitment cause reward sentiments to track punitive sentiments?

No. If labor recruitment were one function of punitive sentiments, then punitive and reward sentiments should track each other strongly and be predicted by SELF-INTEREST IN GROUP GOAL. But in fact, punitive and reward sentiments were uncorrelated in the defensive scenario ($r = .079$, $P = .186$) and only weakly correlated in the offensive scenario ($r = .165$, $P = .005$). To see whether this latter correlation is a real consequence of labor recruitment adaptations, one must first remove those components of the correlation that are irrelevant to the labor recruitment hypothesis. [Each sentiment (reward and punishment) is triggered by a different predictor variable (see Sections 3.2 and 3.6), but these predictor variables are correlated with one another (see Section 3.1). This could create a spurious correlation between reward and punitive sentiments.]

When this is done, the (already weak) correlation between PUNISH NONPARTICIPANTS and REWARD PARTICIPANTS effectively disappears, showing that it was spurious — a side effect of the correlation between predictor variables. The partial correlations between PUNISH NONPARTICIPANTS and REWARD PARTICIPANTS, controlling for the effects of WILLINGNESS TO PARTICIPATE, approximate to zero (partial r's: $r_{defensive} = .011$, $P = .82$; $r_{offensive} = .085$, $P = .061$). Sentiments for punishment and reward were also uncorrelated when the effects of WILLINGNESS TO PARTICIPATE remained, but the effects of SELF-INTEREST IN GROUP GOAL were removed (partial r's: $r_{defensive} = .008$, $P = .89$; $r_{offensive} = .08$, $P = .168$) — as one would expect if reward were unsuitable for preventing outcompetition by free riders.

3.6. Does the perception that one will individually benefit from a collective action predict wish to reward?

Yes. SELF-INTEREST IN GROUP GOAL was positively and significantly correlated with REWARD PARTICIPANTS ($r_{defensive} = .296$, $r_{offensive} = .369$, P's $< .001$). This correlation remained strong, even after controlling for the effects of WILLINGNESS TO PARTICIPATE (partial r's: $r_{defensive} = .272$, $r_{offensive} = .351$, P's $< .001$). Thus, although willingness to participate in a group action does not predict a pro-reward sentiment, perceived self-interest in the outcome of the group action does, and this effect is independent of willingness to participate.

3.7. Were any demographic variables correlated with either punitive sentiment or wish to reward?

None of the demographic variables were useful predictors: neither PUNISH NONPARTI-CIPANTS nor REWARD PARTICIPANTS was significantly correlated with birth order (firstborns vs. laterborns), ethnicity (non-Whites vs. Whites), age, or annual parental income in either scenario (P's $> .05$).

3.8. Were there any sex differences?

Although sex did not predict REWARD PARTICIPANTS in either scenario (P's $>.186$), females did score significantly lower in PUNISH NONPARTICIPANTS in both scenarios (males coded as 1, females as 2; $r_{defensive} = -.291$, $r_{offensive} = -.211$, P's $< .001$). Much of this difference had to do with the fact that females also scored significantly lower in WILLING-NESS TO PARTICIPATE, which, as reported above, predicts PUNISH NONPARTICIPANTS [WILLINGNESS TO PARTICIPATE: female vs. male means: 2.80 vs. 3.80 (defensive), 2.21 vs. 2.96 (offensive); both differences in means are significant (t test for equality of means, P's $< .002$)]. However, even when controlling for WILLINGNESS TO PARTICIPATE, the variance in PUNISH NONPARTICIPANTS predicted by sex was significant in the defensive scenario (partial $r = -.196$, $P = .001$) and marginally so in the offensive scenario (partial $r = -.115$, $P = .054$), that is, women were slightly less motivated to punish nonparticipants, even after controlling for participation. Nevertheless, it is interesting to note that, while sex was somewhat predictive of PUNISH NONPARTICIPANTS, the correlation between WILL-INGNESS TO PARTICIPATE and PUNISH NONPARTICIPANTS was strong for both sexes and close to the value when the sexes are combined: .561 for females and .572 for males in the defensive scenario (.597 combined) and .635 for females and .631 for males in the offensive scenario (.648 combined; all P's $< .001$). There was no significant difference between the sexes in the size of these correlations (P's of ΔF due to sex $> .547$). The partial r's for these variables were also similar for both sexes (defensive: male $= .558$, female $= .461$, com-bined $= .548$; offensive: male $= .598$, female $= .609$, combined $= .623$). (Indeed, there was no significant difference between males and females for any of the 16 cells in Table 1.) Thus, although the scenarios used involved warfare, there was nothing male-specific about the computational connection between participation and punitive sentiment.

4. Discussion

The results were surprisingly clear cut. Subjects' punitive sentiments sensitively tracked their risk of suffering a fitness disadvantage relative to free riders in a collective action and did not track variables suggested by other functions or theories.

4.1. Adaptations for eliminating the free rider fitness advantage: evidence of special design

As any functional model of collective action would predict, the extent to which individuals believed they would benefit from a successful collective action predicted how willing they were to participate in this action. Moreover, both of these variables showed a simple correlation with support for punishing nonparticipants. Note, however, that the simple correlation was much higher for willingness to participate than for perceived self-interest. Moreover, the *only* predictor that made an independent contribution to punitive sentiment was willingness to participate. When we statistically controlled for the effects of perceived self-interest, the correlation between willingness to participate and punitive sentiment remained high (partial r's .548 and .623 compared to simple r's .597 and .648). In contrast, when we statistically controlled for the effects of willingness to participate, the correlation between perceived self-interest and punitive sentiment vanished (partial r's .092 and .092 compared to simple r's .296 and .246).

Precision in the match between the design of a system and a proposed adaptive function is a necessary condition for demonstrating that that system is an adaptation, and for demonstrating what that adaptation's function is (Williams, 1966). An adaptation engineered to prevent a design that causes participation in collective actions from being outcompeted by free riders should key willingness to participate in a collective action precisely to support for the punishment of free riders. That is, the relationship between these variables should be specific and selective. It was. For example:

4.1.1. Selectivity of the participation–punishment link

Although reward and punishment are both time-honored incentive systems, willingness to participate in a collective action predicted the desire to punish free riders but not the desire to reward those who participated. The correlation between willingness to participate and support for rewards was low, and it disappeared once we statistically controlled for the effects of perceived self-interest (partial r's .010 and .025 compared to simple r's .121 and .125). Thus, the effect of willingness to participate on moral intuitions and incentives was selective: It activated punitive sentiments toward free riders, without activating pro-reward sentiments toward participants.

4.1.2. Specificity of the punishment response

The punitive sentiment activated was specific to free riders in a particular collective action. Willingness to participate activated punitive sentiment toward free riders but not punitive sentiments in general (as measured by attitudes toward punishing crimes). Although there was a small correlation between willingness to participate in a collective action and general punitiveness, this effect disappeared once we statistically controlled for the key variable, that is, the extent to which subjects supported punishment of nonparticipants in a collective action (partial r's .065 and .035 compared to simple r's .175 and .179).

4.1.3. Precision of response

Willingness to participate was the *only* variable that independently predicted the motivation to punish free riders. None of the demographic variables (some of which were suggested by alternative theories of punitive sentiment; Carroll et al., 1987; Davis et al., 1993; Sulloway, 1996) predicted support for punishing free riders. Nor did perceived self-interest, once the effects of willingness to participate were removed.

4.1.4. Uniformity of response

Although women expressed less overall support for punishment than men (even controlling for the fact that they were less likely to be willing to serve in the military), the correlation between willingness to participate in a collective action and support for punishment of free riders was just as strong in women as in men.

In other words, the relationship between willingness to participate in a collective action and desire to punish free riders was specific, selective, and uniform. This evidence of special design suggests the presence of an adaptation that was designed for eliminating the adverse fitness differentials that producers would otherwise incur relative to free riders in collective action contexts.

4.2. Is there evidence that punitive sentiment was also designed to encourage participation?

There was no support in these data for the hypothesis that punitive sentiment toward nonparticipants was *designed* to encourage the participation of others in a collective action. Punishment may sometimes have the *effect* of encouraging reluctant non-free riders to participate. But in this research, we are attempting to apply Williams' (1966) adaptationist program: We are trying to distinguish between an adaptation's design features and any incidental side effects it might have, whether beneficial or not.

If punitive sentiment were designed to encourage participation, one would expect the extent to which individuals perceive a collective action to be in their self-interest to be correlated with their degree of punitive sentiment. This was not the case: There was no correlation between individuals' self-interest in a group goal and their punitive sentiment, once we controlled for the effects of their willingness to participate.

That encouraging participation is a (beneficial) byproduct of punishment rather than its primary adaptive function receives further support from experimental economics. Fehr and Gächter (2000a) have shown that the possibility of punishment does encourage higher levels of participation in public goods games but only by discouraging contributions less than the average of the other group members (see also Kurzban et al., 2001). Individuals were punished to the extent that they contributed less than their "fair share" (i.e., the average contribution of other group members); but they were rarely punished for contributions that were at or above that group average. This result is clearly consistent with the function of preventing outcompetition by free riders. It is not, however, what one would expect if the function of punitive sentiments was to recruit optimal participation.

If motivating optimal participation were the selection pressure responsible for designing punitive sentiments, then one should feel punitive toward anyone contributing below the optimum. In Fehr and Gächter's games, an individual benefits the most when others contribute everything. Thus, each individual should view the optimum level of participation by others as the maximum contribution. Nevertheless, there was no pattern of punishing all or even most deviations from this optimum. Punishment was rarely delivered upon those who had contributed their "fair share," even though this amount was almost always well below the optimal contribution.

Logically, why should "fair share" contributors be exempt from punishment? The optimal recruitment function predicts that subjects will feel punitive even toward individuals who are contributing their fair share, as long as they would benefit by these individuals contributing even more. There is no intrinsic reason that circuitry well designed for optimal recruitment would block punitive sentiments toward a person whose contribution is well below the optimum but above whatever the group average happens to be.

If future research confirms this result, then it would show that the trigger for punishment lies in making contributions lower than the average. But this specific trigger point emerges more naturally in an analytical sense from the function of preventing outcompetition by free riders than from the function of encouraging optimal contributions. An individual cannot be a fitness free rider with respect to the group if s/he is contributing at or above the average level[2], but can easily be contributing suboptimally. Although many notions of fairness are conceptually possible (and have been proposed by social theorists), we suggest that terms such as "fair share" and "exploitation" derive their special psychological resonance and rhetorical power from their connection to the evolved circuitry that defends against the threat of adverse fitness differentials posed by free riders.

In the absence of the ability to punish, reducing one's own contribution is the only defense left against outcompetition by free riders. We think that this motivation to reduce contributions is, like punishment, an evolved defense against the proliferation of free rider designs. Indeed, experiments where punishment is not an option show that participants who encounter free riders do indeed reduce their own contributions to the public good (Fehr & Gächter, 2000a; Kurzban et al., 2001). But in a world where punishment is impossible, an inevitable byproduct of this defense is that cooperation — which starts out fairly high in

---

[2] To switch from a group to an individual frame, the criterion for developing a punitive sentiment toward person j should be "did person j contribute less than me," given that person j sufficiently benefits from the group action. If other criteria need to be met (e.g., sufficient social support for punishing an individual) before the sentiment is prudently expressed in punitive action, then this would appear as punishment of those below the *group* average. If the function is redressing adverse fitness differentials, then the motivation should be proportionate to the fitness differential. Assuming that differences in benefit vary randomly across events, this may often reduce to the difference between own contribution and the other's contribution.

public goods games—will eventually unravel (Kurzban et al., 2001). In contrast, cooperation can be sustained when punishment is possible because one can defend against free riders without reducing one's own contribution. This provides a parsimonious explanation for the fact that participation in public goods games (and the net benefit received by each individual) is higher when punishment is possible (Fehr & Gächter, 2000a; Kurzban et al., 2001)—without invoking the additional hypothesis that punitive sentiment evolved to encourage participation.

There is considerable a priori plausibility to the hypothesis that punitive sentiments evolved to serve both participation encouragement and free rider fitness reduction functions, and such a view may ultimately be vindicated in a more comprehensive research program. The existence of some punitive system for labor recruitment would plausibly be adaptive, and may be revealed by new methods. (It may be that while inverting adverse fitness differentials is the primary function, the cost of the punishment system is to some extent offset by labor recruitment. If this were true, punitive sentiments should be more easily acted upon when they also serve a labor recruitment function.) Nevertheless, taken as a whole, the data discussed cast doubt on the hypothesis that the motivation to punish free riders was designed, even secondarily, to accomplish labor recruitment. When the two functions are analyzed separately, the available evidence only provides support for the hypothesis that the motivation to punish free riders was designed for preventing the emergence of fitness advantages for free riders over contributors.

4.3. Evidence of a separate adaptation for producing pro-reward sentiments

This does not, however, mean that there are no adaptations for encouraging participation. Indeed, the data suggest that sentiments for rewarding participants in a collective action may have exactly this function. The perception that one will individually benefit from a successful collective action did predict support for rewarding participants, and this was true even after we statistically controlled for willingness to participate (partial r's .272 and .351 compared to simple r's .296 and .369). Yet, willingness to participate in a collective action did not predict support for rewarding participants, once we controlled for self-interest in seeing the goal achieved. This is consistent with the notion that people resort to positive incentives for participation when they have an interest in the goal being achieved yet cannot (or will not) participate in the collective action themselves.

The hypothesis that there are two independent adaptations at work—punishment circuitry designed to defend against free riders and a reward sentiment designed to encourage participation—is supported by the dissociation displayed in Fig. 1.

4.4. Rational choice fails to explain the design of punitive sentiments in collective action contexts

Evidence that people's sentiments and behavior appear well designed to solve an adaptive problem sometimes elicits the following response: *It is implausible and unparsimonious to argue that there are specialized adaptations for this purpose; instead, people just figure out*

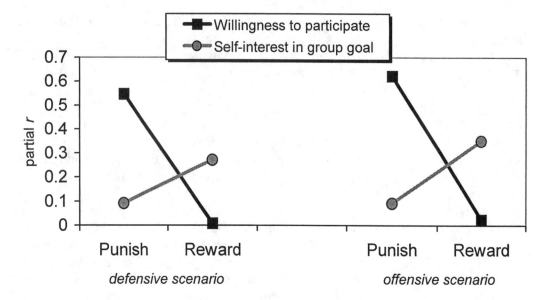

Fig. 1. Partial r's indicate the effect of each predictor variable—controlling for the other—on each outcome variable. The crossover indicates a clear dissociation. Punitive sentiment is independently predicted by willingness to participate, but not by self-interest in the group goal. Pro-reward sentiment is independently predicted by self-interest in the group goal, but not by willingness to participate. This suggests that, in a collective action context, pro-reward sentiments and punitive sentiments are generated by two different adaptations.

which sentiments and choices are in their best interest. While seductive, this proposal is problematic as an alternative hypothesis. It fails to deliver on precisely what is at issue: What is the structure of the neurocognitive machinery whereby individuals "figure it out"? Consequently, it is too ill-defined to count as a proper alternative hypothesis about mechanisms. In fact, most rational choice style theories posit a form of unbounded rationality that is impossible to implement computationally (Cosmides & Tooby, 1987; Gigerenzer & Selten, 2001).

Nevertheless, it is illuminating to see how far one can go in empirically evaluating this family of hypotheses. This can be done by analyzing rational choice theory not as a (hopelessly) vague proposal about architecture but rather as a task analysis of what a general payoff-maximizing architecture, free of inherited specializations and defaults, should be designed to do. Rational choice theories posit that there is computational machinery that is able to assume whatever form is necessary to maximize individual payoffs, and which chooses (or deploys) sentiments (or other mental entities, such as decision rules) on the basis of whether they accomplish this function. Most critically, it does this solely on the basis of incentives and information available to the individual over the course of the lifespan: By hypothesis, this decisional machinery lacks inherited, evolved specializations and so does not make default assumptions that were ancestrally reliable (but may now be violated) about the structure of environments and likely payoffs. This alternative *can* be evaluated, because a system designed to maximize individual payoffs in current collective action contexts would predict different sets of sentiments than one designed to eliminate adverse fitness differentials under ancestral conditions. This is true whether one assumes punitive sentiments operate by motivating the individual who has them (1) to personally inflict punishment or (2) to advocate a general regime of norms that are applied to everyone, including oneself. Indeed, we can also evaluate a more relaxed form of the rational choice viewpoint — that is, that these results are explained by the hypothesis that people favor acts, rules, and norms that are in their interest, even if they do not always do this in a rationally cost-effective manner.

The results that decide against the view that punitive sentiments evolved to optimize participant recruitment also falsify the view that they are produced by a general-purpose rational choice system. More specifically:

1. A rational agent should only punish noncooperation when the payoffs to that agent in terms of the benefits of increased future cooperation exceed the costs to that specific agent of punishing. This seems unlikely to be true in the great majority of cases, for example, when the social group is large, as it is in most residential groups, coalitions, political units, and so on (modern and ancestral). Testing the sensitivity of subjects to this condition, experimental economists have established that people regularly incur costs to punish free riders, even when they know they will not interact with these individuals again. The absence of future interactions means punishing others will not gain them benefits in the form of higher levels of future experienced cooperation, and so punishers in these contexts do not recoup the costs they expended on punishment (Fehr & Gächter, 2000a; Gintis, 2000). This form of spite, expressed even on the last move of an interaction, cannot be explained by a desire to maximize individual payoffs. It can, however, result from adaptations designed to reverse adverse fitness differentials and prevent outcompetition by free riders. In this case, the issue is preventing the malefactor from getting away with his or her unfair winnings. In contrast, for rational choice, the issue is maximizing present and future payoffs — and payoffs to the individual, not payoffs to one design relative to another. [Experimental economists have established that spiteful punishment also occurs in dyadic cooperation (Hoffman, McCabe, & Smith, 1998), suggesting that reversing adverse fitness differentials may be a significant factor in the evolution of dyadic reciprocation as well.]

2. Leaving aside the irrationality of incurring unreimbursed costs of punishment, rational choice predicts that the targets of punitive sentiments should be those individuals who could increase their levels of cooperation to the benefit of the rational agent. Clearly, this includes all individuals who contribute less than the optimum, including those who contribute at or above the group average. Yet, as discussed above, subjects in public goods games rarely punished contributions in this zone. This otherwise puzzling result makes sense if punitive sentiments were instead designed to eliminate ancestral fitness advantages of free rider designs rather than to maximize joint payoffs.

3. Most critically, if punitive sentiments were produced by a system designed to maximize individual payoffs, then rational choice theory straightforwardly predicts that self-interest in the group goal should regulate punitive sentiments. This is the most basic prediction, even for the relaxed form of the rational choice approach. However, in this study, self-interest in the group goal did not independently predict punitive sentiments.

4. Moreover, willingness to participate did independently predict punitive sentiments. Yet rational choice does not offer a good explanation for why participation per se rather than self-interest creates punitive sentiment toward nonparticipants.[3] On the contrary: To base punitive sentiments on willingness to participate *independent of expected gain* is to operate independent of self-interest, in a way that parallels the sunk cost fallacy. Sentiments are rationally deployed only as a function of one's expected gain from the project's success, and not as a function of how much effort one has or will expend, regardless of expected gains. In contrast, this relationship between participation and punitive sentiment is a direct prediction of the hypothesis that the function of punitive sentiments is to eliminate the fitness advantage of free riders.

5. Providing incentives to increase other people's participation is costly. However, a system designed to maximize individual payoffs should (aside from issues of cost-effectiveness) be intrinsically indifferent to whether a unit of cost is deployed to punish nonparticipants or to reward participants. This suggests that punishment and reward sentiments should track each other, and be triggered by the same variables. Neither was true in our data.

In interpreting our scenarios, subjects may have assumed that the punishments and rewards would be dispensed by the government. Can any of the difficult results noted above be explained away by assuming that the sentiments produced by a rational choice system operate by motivating one to advocate a general regime of norms?

The norms advocated would have to be self-beneficial, even though they are applied to everyone, including oneself. If self-beneficial norm establishment is the function of punitive sentiments, then perhaps nonparticipants should avoid advocating punishment, lest this community-enforced punishment norm be visited on them. On first pass, this seems to explain one otherwise puzzling finding: that punitive sentiments are high only in those willing to participate. On closer inspection, however, it becomes clear that this line of argument cannot rescue the rational choice view. The following results argue against the notion that sentiments for punishment and reward are produced by a system designed to advocate norms that are self-serving in the rational choice sense:

6. The self-serving norms approach predicts that punitive sentiment will be high only in individuals who feel they would benefit from the group goal's attainment *and* are willing to participate. That is, the two predictor variables should predict high punitive sentiment only when they co-occur (there should be an interaction, but no main effects). This was not the case: after all, willingness to participate predicted punitiveness *independent of self-interest in the group goal*, and there was no two-way interaction (P's > .50). (This finding was not due to high covariance between the predictor variables in the data set: The correlation between self-interest in group goal and willingness to participate was only .28–.38).

---

[3] At least insofar as punitive sentiments are designed to motivate the personal infliction of punishment on others, rather than norm creation. A motivation to punish others would not punish itself, and so could easily be designed to punish others for nonparticipation while being a nonparticipant.

7. The norm approach presumes that those who benefit from a public good are better off when there is a punishment norm and will therefore advocate one, unless by doing so they risk being punished themselves. Note, however, that if others believe you are exempt from participation, then you do not risk advocating your own punishment by supporting the punishment of free riders. The correlation between willingness to participate and punitive sentiment should therefore be lower — or even nonexistent — for those who are exempt: Exempt nonparticipants who will benefit from a public good can — and should — advocate punishment of nonexempt nonparticipants. But our data do not support this prediction. In the USA, women have traditionally been exempt from military conscription. Female subjects should therefore have a greater rational expectation that they will be exempt from participating in a war as soldiers than men will, i.e., that they will not be punished for being nonparticipants. Yet, the correlation between participation and punitive sentiment was just as strong in female subjects as in male subjects. This undermines the self-serving norm explanation. In contrast, this result makes sense if women's responses are not based on incentives in the modern world, but instead reflect a psychological design that ancestrally prevented out competition by free riders.

Indeed, although not probed in this study, it seems very likely that our psychology of collective action recognizes the distinction between free riding and nonparticipation for excusable reasons. The self-serving norm theory predicts that, to the extent that participants and the exempt both benefit from the provision of a public good, they should experience equal intensities of punitiveness toward free riders. In contrast, the hypothesis that punitiveness is a defense for participant designs against outcompetition by free riders predicts that participants — but not nonparticipants (exempt or not) — should experience the most intense punitive sentiment.

8. The notion that the mind contains a system that deploys sentiments insofar as they create payoff-maximizing norms is most damaged by the results pertaining to pro-reward sentiments. If such a system existed, it would surely use degree of participation to trigger sentiments for rewarding participants (whether or not it uses participation as a trigger for punitive sentiments). Those willing to participate should favor community rewards for participation because this norm is in their self-interest: They would be among the beneficiaries, thereby receiving payoffs above and beyond the provision of the public good itself. Yet willingness to participate did not independently predict pro-reward sentiment. In contrast, this otherwise puzzling result is a prediction of the outcompetition prevention function. If eliminating adverse fitness differentials is the dominating adaptive problem in collective action contexts, then willingness to participate should inhibit the desire to reward those who contribute, but contribute less. This is because transferring rewards from some participants to participants who contribute less preserves or even amplifies the fitness differentials accruing to free riders.[4]

---

[4] We predicted no relationship, rather than a negative one, between willingness to participate and pro-reward sentiment because in this study the rewards are coming out of a communal pocket rather than the individual's. This lessens the cost incurred by an individual of providing rewards; nevertheless, the provision of rewards to encourage more participation still preserves the relative fitness advantage of free riders.

In short, the rational choice hypothesis fails, in eight different ways, to explain the pattern of punitive and pro-reward sentiments elicited by collective action contexts in this and other studies.

4.5. Will the results of this study generalize?

Although the results reported here are robust and unambiguous, it will be important to see how well they generalize to other collective action contexts. This survey used a collective action problem involving a nation-state, because in the population tested, this was a common point of reference and also likely to elicit enough variation in willingness to participate to see whether willingness would predict punitive sentiment. Obviously, however, the hypothesis should be tested among people living in conditions more representative of the ancestral social environments in which these adaptations evolved (e.g., small-scale or foraging societies). If punitiveness toward nonparticipants operated as an anti-free rider device in ancestral collective action contexts, then its operation as such should be clearly observable in social environments that resemble those of the ancestral past more closely. A study of this kind is underway in the Ecuadorian Amazon, combining survey data with observations of behavioral choices and outcomes. The results so far are highly consistent with those presented herein.

Some argue that behavioral data are inherently reliable, while survey data — even when responses are anonymous — are worthless because subjects may lie. Our own view is that both kinds of data are valuable and complementary. Indeed, we hope the present study illustrates how survey data can fill in the blanks left by aggregate behavioral data and vice versa. There are several problems with the view that our results could be explained as deception. First, it carries no directional prediction; at best, it would introduce noise in the data (for the questions we asked, there is no consensual, "socially desirable" answer). Second, because we are interested in whether an increase in one variable is associated with an increase in another (controlling for a third!), subjects would have to be clairvoyant in order to deceive *in just the right way* that their answers would mesh with those of others to create the partial correlations found. Third, the possibility of lying or other forms of invalidity does not distinguish surveys from behavioral data in experimental games: People can "lie" in experimental games, that is, behave playfully, maliciously, or unrepresentatively, in the sense of making choices they would not make in real life. The idea that people indulge in these motivations and values in surveys but not in experimental games because of payments — often quite small — seems unlikely, given the large sums people routinely pay to indulge these motivations in other contexts. [Moreover, experienced experimentalists know all too well that subjects often respond to narrow features of the experimental situation differently than they would to those features of the world to which the experimenters imagine the task corresponds (Hoffman et al., 1998).] Even worse, in an experimental game — or in real life — behavioral indices of the predictor variables are hopelessly confounded: One's degree of participation should be correlated with one's self-interest in the group goal, preventing the experimenter from discovering whether punitive sentiment is triggered by one variable but not the other. In short, different approaches are complementary and powerful when combined, with valid conclusions emerging from converging lines of evidence developed from applying a diversity of methods.

4.6. Can the results help decide between alternative selectionist theories of the evolution of collective action?

Evidence of special design in an adaptation can sometimes allow one to choose between alternative theories about selection pressures. Although the results presented herein are broadly consistent with both individual and group selection theories, it does seem fair to say that the fit between design and selectionist model is tighter in most respects for individual than group level theories.

Most theories of the evolution of collective action that emphasize selection at the individual level *require* adaptations that adjust an individual's willingness to punish free riders so that it reflects that individual's risk of being outcompeted by them (Tooby & Cosmides, 1988, 1996). Such theories assume that humans evolved in small social groups in which they would have had repeated interactions with the same individuals and that adaptations for collective action will reflect this fact, generating behavior that, while perhaps not adaptive in modern nation states or experimental laboratories, would have been adaptive ancestrally (for an application of this line of reasoning to results in experimental economics, see Hoffman et al., 1998).

Some group selection models also assume that punishment will be delivered by those who cooperate; the "strong reciprocity" model proposed by Gintis (2000) is an example. However, this model requires that *group* benefits outweigh *group* costs and assumes that strong reciprocators cooperate and punish even when this involves a penalty to their within-group fitness. Indeed, the model as presented only allows for discrete, and not graded, responses (i.e., cooperate or not). Thus, it does not require adaptations that calibrate *how much* an individual is willing to punish to the *amount* of his or her own personal sacrifice. Moreover, while the Gintis model does assume that cooperation and punishment are provided by the same individual at the phenotypic level, it is not clear that his or other group selection models require this. As the case of warriors and workers within the same species of ant illustrates, a uniform genotype can give rise to different phenotypic morphs, each with a differentiated function. Thus, for one group to out-compete another in fitness production, such models require that the group includes both cooperators and punishers, but it is not clear that these functions need to be localized within the *same* individuals.

One fundamental question is left unaddressed in this analysis: Why don't second-order free riders (i.e., those who do not punish free riders) proliferate at the expense of those equipped with punitive sentiments? This will be addressed in further work.

The results presented herein are suggestive, not conclusive. Future studies, providing more detailed information about the design of adaptations for collective action, may be better able to adjudicate between different selectionist theories. Nevertheless, a complex pattern of evidence has been developed which supports the hypothesis that punitive sentiments in collective action contexts evolved to reverse the fitness advantages that accrue to free riders over producers. This suggests that an adaptationist analysis of the psychology of collective action may prove illuminating.

5. Conclusion

In sum, we think that the existing evidence, on balance, supports the following conclusions: There is a suite of adaptations that evolved to allow individuals to benefit from engaging cooperatively in collective actions. This suite includes a motivational subsystem that produces punitive sentiments specifically targeted at free riders. The primary function of this circuitry is to prevent free rider designs from having higher fitness than cooperator designs. Moreover, the regulatory effects of the variable underlying punitive sentiments appear narrowly tailored to this anti-free rider function: Willingness to participate did predict punitive sentiments, but did not predict support for rewarding collective action participants or for punishment outside a specific collective action context. This punitive subsystem lacked evidence of special design for alternative adaptive functions, such as optimizing participation in collective actions. While the secondary effect this system sometimes has of increasing contributions to collective efforts may be one way the system offsets its cost, there is no evidence that it is the primary function of punitive sentiments. However, existing evidence supports the view that a separate motivational subsystem evolved to solve the problem of labor recruitment through pro-reward rather than punitive sentiments. Finally, despite the consistency of these results, it nevertheless remains possible that experimenting with other contexts will elicit evidence of a motivational subsystem that is designed to deploy punitive sentiments in order to recruit labor into collective actions.

Acknowledgments

We gratefully acknowledge Don Brown, Napoleon Chagnon, Nancy Collins, Brad Duchaine, Adam Fox, Ed Hagen, Nickie Hess, Rob Kurzban, Hassan Lopez, David Price, Don Symons, and Tina Wells for their kind assistance. This research was supported by a Jacob K. Javits Fellowship from the U.S. Department of Education, by the James S. McDonnell Foundation, the National Science Foundation (#BNS9157-449), the Harry Frank Guggenheim Foundation, and the UCSB Office of Research (Research Across Disciplines Program: Evolution and the Social Mind).

Appendix

Defensive scenario: Imagine that a few years from now, the Russian people elect a new, warlike dictator who claims that Alaska should rightfully belong to Russia. Under this dictator, Russia invades and conquers Alaska. There is good evidence that Russia also intends to conquer more US territory, in addition to Alaska. In response to this invasion, the USA declares war on Russia. But because this war was unexpected, the USA has allowed its army to get relatively small, and it must start drafting US citizens in order to have a chance of winning this war. How would you feel about this war?

Offensive scenario: Imagine that a few years from now, several oil-rich Middle Eastern countries get together and decide that to increase profits, they will dramatically raise the price of their oil. This price increase devastates US industry and causes high inflation in the USA. US gas prices triple, and several US oil companies go bankrupt. After talks with these Middle Eastern countries fail, the USA declares war on them. But war was unexpected, so the USA has allowed its army to get relatively small, and it must start drafting US citizens in order to have a chance of victory. How would you feel about this war?

References

Alexander, R. D. (1987). *The biology of moral systems*. Hawthorne, NY: Aldine de Gruyter.

Andreoni, J. (1990). Impure altruism and donations to public goods — a theory of warm-glow giving. *Economic Journal, 100*, 464–477.

Andreoni, J. (1995). Cooperation in public goods experiments: kindness or confusion. *American Economic Review, 85*, 891–904.

Boyd, R., & Richerson, P. J. (1992). Punishment allows the evolution of cooperation (or anything else) in sizable groups. *Ethology and Sociobiology, 13*, 171–195.

Carroll, J. S., Perkowitz, W. T., Lurigio, A. J., & Weaver, F. M. (1987). Sentencing goals, causal attributions, ideology, and personality. *Journal of Personality and Social Psychology, 52*, 107–118.

Chagnon, N. (1988). Life histories, blood revenge, and warfare in a tribal population. *Science, 239*, 985–992.

Chagnon, N. (1997). *The Yanomamo: case studies in cultural anthropology*. New York: Harcourt.

Cosmides, L., & Tooby, J. (1987). From evolution to behavior: evolutionary psychology as the missing link. In: J. Dupre (Ed.), *The latest on the best: essays on evolution and optimality* (pp. 277–306). Cambridge, MA: MIT Press.

Cronk, L. (1994). Evolutionary theories of morality and the manipulative use of signals. *Zygon, 29*, 81–101.

Davis, T. L., Severy, L. J., Kraus, S. J., & Whitaker, J. M. (1993). Predictors of sentencing decisions: the beliefs, personality variables, and demographic factors of juvenile justice personnel. *Journal of Applied Social Psychology, 23*, 451–477.

Dawes, R. M., Orbell, J. M., & Van de Kragt, J. C. (1986). Organizing groups for collective action. *American Political Science Review, 80*, 1171–1185.

Fehr, E., & Gächter, S. (2000a). Cooperation and punishment in public goods experiments. *American Economic Review, 90*, 980–994.

Fehr, E., & Gächter, S. (2000b). Fairness and retaliation: the economics of reciprocity. *Journal of Economic Perspectives, 14*, 159–181.

Frank, R. (1988). *Passions within reason: the strategic role of the emotions*. New York: Norton.

Gigerenzer, G., & Selten, R. (Eds.) (2001). *Bounded rationality: the adaptive toolbox*. Cambridge, MA: MIT Press.

Gintis, H. (2000). Strong reciprocity and human sociality. *Journal of Theoretical Biology, 206*, 169–179.

Gurven, M., Hill, K., Kaplan, H., Hurtado, A., & Lyles, R. (2000). Food transfers among Hiwi foragers of Venezuela: tests of reciprocity. *Human Ecology, 28*, 171–218.

Hardin, G. (1968). The tragedy of the commons. *Science, 162*, 1243–1248.

Harner, M. J. (1984). *The Jívaro, people of the sacred waterfalls*. Berkeley: University of California Press.

Hawkes, K. (1993). Why hunter-gatherers work — an ancient version of the problem of public goods. *Current Anthropology, 34*, 341–361.

Henrich, J., & Boyd, R. (2001). Why people punish defectors: weak conformist transmission can stabilize costly enforcement of norms in cooperative dilemmas. *Journal of Theoretical Biology, 208*, 79–89.

Hirshleifer, D., & Rasmusen, E. (1989). Cooperation in a repeated prisoners dilemma with ostracism. *Journal of Economic Behavior and Organization, 12*, 87–106.

Hirshleifer, J. (1987). On the emotions as guarantors of threats and promises. In: J. Dupre (Ed.), *The latest on the best: essays on evolution and optimality* (pp. 307–326). Cambridge, MA: MIT Press.

Hoffman, E., McCabe, K., & Smith, V. (1998). Behavioral foundations of reciprocity: experimental economics and evolutionary psychology. *Economic Inquiry, 36*, 335–352.

Holmberg, A. (1969). *Nomads of the long blow: the Siriono of eastern Bolivia*. Garden City, NY: Natural History Press.

Irons, W. (1991). How did morality evolve? *Zygon, 26*, 49–89.

Keeley, L. H. (1996). *War before civilization: the myth of the peaceful savage*. Oxford: Oxford Univ. Press.

Kelly, R. L. (1995). *The foraging spectrum: diversity in hunter-gatherer lifeways*. Washington: Smithsonian Institution Press.

Kurzban, R., McCabe, K., Smith, V., & Wilson, B. (2001). Incremental commitment in a real-time public goods game. *Personality and Social Psychology Bulletin, 27* (12), 1662–1673.

Ledyard, J. (1995). Public goods: a survey of experimental research. In: J. H. Kagel, & A. E. Roth (Eds.), *The handbook of experimental economics* (pp. 111–194). Princeton, NJ: Princeton Univ. Press.

Lee, R., & DeVore, I. (Eds.) (1968). *Man the hunter*. Chicago: Aldine.

Lemonnier, P. (1996). Food, competition, and the status of food in New Guinea. In: P. W. Wiessner, & W. Schiefenhövel (Eds.), *Food and the status quest: an interdisciplinary perspective*. Providence: Berghahn Books.

Olson, M. (1965). *The logic of collective action: public goods and the theory of groups*. Cambridge: Harvard Univ. Press.

Ostrom, E. (1998). A behavioral approach to the rational choice theory of collective action. *American Political Science Review, 92*, 1–22.

Ostrom, E., Walker, J., & Gardner, R. (1992). Covenants with and without a sword: self-governance is possible. *American Political Science Review, 86*, 404–417.

Patton, J. Q. (1996). *Thoughtful warriors: status, warriorship, and alliance in the Ecuadorian Amazon*. Doctoral dissertation, Department of Anthropology, University of California, Santa Barbara.

Patton, J. Q. (2000). Reciprocal altruism and warfare: a case from the Ecuadorian Amazon. In: L. Cronk, N. A. Chagnon, & W. Irons (Eds.), *Adaptation and human behavior: an anthropological perspective* (pp. 417–436). New York: Aldine de Gruyter.

Sato, K. (1987). Distribution of the cost of maintaining common resources. *Journal of Experimental Social Psychology, 23*, 19–31.

Smith, E. A. (1985). Inuit foraging groups: some simple models incorporating conflicts of interest, relatedness, and central-place sharing. *Ethology and Sociobiology, 6*, 37–57.

Smole, W. J. (1976). *The Yanoama Indians: a cultural geography*. Austin: University of Texas Press.

Sober, E., & Wilson, D. S. (1998). *Unto others: the evolution and psychology of unselfish behavior*. Cambridge: Harvard Univ. Press.

Stern, P. C. (1995). Why do people sacrifice for their nations? *Political Psychology, 16*, 217–235.

Sugiyama, L. S. (1996). *In search of the adapted mind: a study of human cognitive adaptations among the Shiwiar of Ecuador and the Yora of Peru*. Doctoral dissertation, Department of Anthropology, University of California, Santa Barbara.

Sulloway, F. (1996). *Born to rebel*. New York: Pantheon.

Tooby, J., & Cosmides, L. (1988). *The evolution of war and its cognitive foundations*. Institute for Evolutionary Studies Technical Report 88-1. Reprinted in Tooby, J. & Cosmides, L. (in press). *Evolutionary psychology: foundational papers*. Cambridge, MA: MIT Press.

Tooby, J., & Cosmides, L. (1989). The innate versus the manifest: how universal does universal have to be? *Behavioral and Brain Sciences, 12*, 36–37.

Tooby, J. & Cosmides, L. (1996). Groups in mind: the evolution of cognitive adaptations for coalitions and status. *Ciba Foundation*, London, England. Symposium #208: *Characterizing human psychological adaptations*.

Watson, J. B. (1971). Tairora: the politics of despotism in a small society. In: R. M. Berndt, & P. Lawrence (Eds.), *Politics in New Guinea* (pp. 224–275). Nedlands: University of Western Australia.

Williams, G. C. (1966). *Adaptation and natural selection*. Princeton: Princeton Univ. Press.

Williams, G. C. (1975). *Sex and evolution*. Princeton: Princeton Univ. Press.

Wrangham, R., & Peterson, D. (1996). *Demonic males: apes and the origins of human violence*. Boston: Houghton Mifflin.

Wright, R. (1994). *The moral animal*. New York: Pantheon.

Yamagishi, T. (1986). The provision of a sanctioning system as a public good. *Journal of Personality and Social Psychology, 51*, 110–116.

Yamagishi, T. (1992). Group size and the provision of a sanctioning system in a social dilemma. In: W. Liebrand, D. Messick, & H. Wilke (Eds.), *Social dilemmas: theoretical issues and research findings* (pp. 267–287). Oxford: Pergamon.

Evolutionary perspectives on human behavior from various disciplines.

Official Journal of the
Human Behavior and Evolution Society

An interdisciplinary journal, *Evolution and Human Behavior* presents peer-reviewed research reports and theory in which evolutionary perspectives are brought to bear on the study of human behavior.

As the official journal of the *Human Behavior and Evolution Society*, *Evolution and Human Behavior* broadens its perspective with quality research from the humanities. You'll also find reports on theoretical and empirical work on other species that throw light on the human experience.

Visit the journal's Web site at
http://www.elsevier.com/locate/ethsoc

Editors-in-Chief: M. Daly and M. Wilson, *McMaster University, Department of Psychology, Hamilton, Ontario, Canada*

Abstracting / Indexing: *Current Contents/Social and Behavioral Sciences, EMBASE, PsycINFO Social Science Citation Index, Sociological Abstracts*

Subscription Information

Volume 23, 2002 • Published bimonthly • ISSN 1090-5138
Subscription Rates:
Individual: US 291 • JYP 34,500 • EUR 260   **Institution:** US 705 • JYP 83,600 • EUR 630

---

3 Easy Ways to Order!

Phone: In US or Canada, call toll-free 1-888-437-4636. • **Outside the US or Canada,** call 1-212-633-3730.

Fax: Fax to 1-212-633-3680 **to order.**

Visit: www.elsevier.com. **Order via the Internet at any time!**

ContentsDirect Now Available.
Elsevier's FREE ContentsDirect service is now available for *Evolution and Human Behavior*. This free e-mail service delivers book and journal tables of contents directly to your PC, providing you with the very latest information on soon-to-be-published research. To register as a new user, visit the ContentsDirect Web site at **http://www.elsevier.com/locate/contentsdirect**.